Sydney Brenner
A life in science

As told to Lewis Wolpert

Edited interview with additional material by Errol C Friedberg and Eleanor Lawrence

Produced by Science Archive Limited

Published by BioMed Central Limited

Produced by Science Archive Limited

Published by BioMed Central Limited

34-42 Cleveland Street, London W1P 6LB, UK http://www.biomedcentral.com/

© Science Archive Limited 2001

Revised edition

British Library Cataloguing in Publication Data.

A catalogue record for this book is available from the British Library.

ISBN 0-9540278-0-9

The complete video autobiography on which this edited interview is based can be accessed from Science Archive through BioMed Central at

http://www.biomedcentral.com/sciencearchive/

Cover image: Sydney Brenner in 1948, before leaving for England.
Project editor: Anita Chakraverty, Ruth King
Designer: Christopher Thorpe
Production: David Forrest

Printed in Singapore

15 14 13 12 10 9 8 7 6 5 4 3 2

Contents

Preface

The latter half of the twentieth century will be remembered as one of the great periods, perhaps the greatest, in the history of biology and Sydney Brenner has been one of the principal contributors to this golden age. This book has been produced from the transcript of a fifteen-hour videotaped autobiography, as told to Lewis Wolpert, Professor of Biology as Applied to Medicine, in the Department of Anatomy and Developmental Biology, University College, London. In editing this transcript, we have strived to capture the highlights of Brenner's long and productive career as one of the pre-eminent biologists of the twentieth century. We have also attempted to capture much of the man – a man endowed with great wit and humour, a strong sense of irreverence, iconoclasm, and a profound appreciation of biology in its many and varied aspects.

We have left Brenner's original words as untouched as possible. In the interests of continuity and coherence, some linking and explanatory passages have been added by Errol Friedberg; these sections are in italic type. We hope that this book will give non-biologists and biologists alike a unique insight into what it was like to be at the heart of this exceptional period in biology.

Errol C Friedberg and Eleanor Lawrence

"I think the most important thing we know about living systems is that they've got genes. It is through the genes that one living system propagates descendants that look like it. The theoretical physicist Richard Feynman once said that the most important thing about matter is that it's built of atoms, and he also remarked that the most important thing about living systems is that they are just parts of matter and that they are built of atoms. But the most important thing about living systems is they've got genes in them. Therefore, in my view, all explanations of living systems have to be couched in that form; in the form of genes. Because it surely must be the oldest observation to mankind; that the first sentient organism would look around him at the natural world and would notice that plants give rise to plants that look like them, that men give rise to other men, that fleas give rise to fleas. So that like produces like is the oldest biological observation. What science has accomplished is to tell us that this happens because organisms contain genes in them and that the future organism is written in this somehow. And 'somehow' is what we have to explain. We have to say not somehow, but how."

Sydney Brenner
Cambridge, 1994

1
Growing up in
South Africa

*The twentieth century is distinguished by two fundamental scientific revolutions –
the first in physics, the second in biology – which have helped to shape the landscape
of human discovery. For one, the key was the atom and its innermost secrets, and for
the other it was the structure of the gene and its workings. Sydney Brenner, born in
South Africa but passing most of his scientific life in England, was one of the key
players in this latter revolution, which gave birth to the science of molecular biology.*

*In the quotation that prefaces this account, Brenner contrasts the physicist's view of
the living world with his own as a biologist. Like others in the "magic circle" of biological revolutionaries, he was greatly attracted by the physicists' ability to cut
through obscuring biological detail to grasp the core of a problem and find new ways
of approaching it. But he remained above all an experimental biologist, with a firm
grasp of biological reality.*

Unlike some of his peers, he has continued to be a productive experimental scientist throughout his career, and his contributions to biology are staggering in their originality, breadth and depth; few biologists have demonstrated such a gift for innovative experimentation. Like all scientists, Brenner suffered his share of experimental and theoretical failures, but much of what he touched turned to gold. He ranks high on everyone's list of scientists whose achievements clearly merit a Nobel Prize but who have never received that accolade.

Brenner's unique style and talents were encouraged and sharpened by his early experience. Born into a family of very modest means in a remote part of the world far from the mainstream of science, he developed a robust sense of intellectual self-reliance and self-discipline. Added to his innate brilliance, this gave him at an early age a profound scepticism that has made him always question received wisdom.

Like many other Eastern European Jews, Brenner's father (a Lithuanian) emigrated from Eastern Europe in the uneasy years preceding the Bolshevik Revolution in Russia, arriving in South Africa in 1910. He had a sister in the United States, but when he got to London he discovered that he could afford the boat fare to South Africa, where he had a brother, but not the more expensive fare to America. In South Africa, according to the grapevine that led back to home, a living, and often a good one, was to be made so he headed there.

Brenner's father settled in the small town of Germiston, just outside Johannesburg, and married an émigré from Latvia. He worked as a cobbler, a trade he practiced all his life. On 13 January 1927, Sydney Brenner, the younger of the two children, was born.

"We lived in two rooms at the back of the shop, as many people lived in those days. I have dim memories of playing in my father's shop, and I can still remember the smell of leather that dominated my entire early life. My mother was a fairly orthodox Jew, but my father was a total agnostic. He didn't practice anything and was totally against religion. We had my grandmother living with us, and she spoke only Russian and Yiddish. So as a child I learned to speak some Russian. One always knew when one's parents and grandmother spoke Russian that it concerned something they didn't want us to hear about. So it became very important to find out what it was!

My father went on working until he was over eighty. He was one of those people who felt that if you stopped working you might as well just stop living. He couldn't read or write at all to the day he died. In fact, when my father was naturalised we had to get a lawyer to fill out the forms. But he had a great aptitude for languages, and he spoke two African languages as well as Afrikaans.

Around the corner from us lived a lady whose husband had been a tailor, but had died. She had known my mother's family in Latvia and I spent quite a lot of time with her. She lived in a tiny room where she cooked for herself. She taught me to read from the newspapers that were on her table – *in lieu* of tablecloths. So by the age of four I could read quite fluently.

My father had a customer called Mrs MacCartney. She saw me reading – I must have been about four and a half – and she told my father that I really should be sent to kindergarten. My father told her that he simply couldn't afford that. But she ran a local kindergarten through one of the churches and said that she would take me in. And so I started going to kindergarten when I was five years old."

Brenner flourished in the South African school system in the small town of Germiston. His intellectual talents were quickly recognised and he was promoted to a level three years ahead of his age. He has dim memories of some rewarding experiences at school, but recalls the less happy ones more vividly. Being rather small in stature (although quite stocky), and considerably younger than his classmates, he had to endure a fair amount of bullying and teasing.

"I simply grew up to be a professional coward. I would agree to anything not to get bullied. I suppose that's a way of withdrawing from a situation, and also allows you to have fantasies about how you might get revenge on all these people!

There were some really awful teachers in my high school. There was a teacher who made us wear ties, for example. I think that my total dislike of ties stems from this period. If you came to his class without a tie he would take the cords from the skylights and tie them around your neck in such a way that your feet were about a quarter of an inch off the ground. So you either strangled or stood on tiptoe all through the class! Such things were pretty standard at that time in South Africa.

I recall my English teacher not liking the way I recited the only poetry that I remembered, which was from *King Lear*. It was this wonderful speech in which Edmund decries the fact that he's a bastard. It's full of words like 'base' and 'bastard' and 'vile', which of course at that age were simply wonderful to enunciate in public – with the correct tone of voice. But if you offended this teacher you had to crawl around the class like a dog and kneel by your chair until you had permission to sit!

The teachers were not really very effective. Of course this was a small school, in a provincial town, in a provincial country, so school wasn't a very stimulating environment at all. During the period in high school I wasn't at the very top of the class. I was good – I was always among the top six. But people never pointed to me and said, 'He's going to be *the* winner.' As it turned out, the people who were thought to be *the* winners in school went on to lives of total intellectual obscurity. This led me to the conclusion in later life that if a student came to me with a First Class degree he still had to prove to me that he could have had a Second Class degree if he'd tried! Book learning and giving it all back in examinations was simply not my *forte*. I realised that what I was being taught in chemistry and physics and so on, was just what was in the books, and was all that you really needed to pass an examination."

The provincialism of South African schooling only encouraged Brenner's natural talent and curiosity. He became quick and diligent at teaching himself, skills that he has practiced ever since.

"The most interesting thing that I can recall from those days is discovering the public library. The world of books has always been very important to me. There were no books at home of course, but I rapidly graduated to the adult library and read voraciously about lots of things. There were two early books that I read while I went through school, which were in the field of science and which I remember very clearly. One was called *The Young Chemist*.[1] This was by a man called Sherwood Taylor and it gave wonderful recipes for how to do chemistry experiments. So I started doing chemistry at the age of ten. By this time we had moved into a house where there was a garage – this was in 1937 – and that's when I started to do chemistry in a serious way. Of course, it was very difficult to get apparatus, but I saved my money and bought a test tube or some reagent

1.   Taylor FS. *The Young Chemist*. London: Nelson & Sons, 1934.

5

every few weeks at the local pharmacy. I remember doing experiments which involved making pigments. I even started doing some biochemistry shortly after that – extracting natural pigments from leaves and petals and so on. I discovered that anthocyanin pigments responded to pH. Needless to say, that was not an original discovery.

But the thing that turned me onto biology was a book called *The Science of Life*, by Wells, Huxley and Wells.[2] I have to confess that I stole it from the public library and told them I'd lost it, because I couldn't afford to buy a copy of it at the time. So I paid the fine instead! The Wells book covered everything that was known about biology. There was the whole thing about physiology – about how things worked. That seemed to me to be very important. But really there was just this fascination with knowledge in itself – that people had actually discovered that there were pigments involved in photosynthesis – and this entire ability to draw the veil apart from nature. I realised in this way that you didn't actually have to ask people how to do things; you could do them yourself. If you could get hold of a book that told you, introduced you to how to do something, you could just go ahead and do it. That's something I have kept with me all my life, because I have never learned anything from going to courses. If I want to learn a new subject I get a book and start doing it. It's advice I always give. When I got interested in computing in the early sixties I started by learning an assembly language and actually programming a computer.

I think that in today's environment nobody can learn anything unless they go to a course – do this in a formal sense. I just never had that experience since there

2. Wells HG, Huxley J, Wells GP. *The Science of Life*. London: Cassell & Co, 1931.

was no one to teach me really. So I cultivated, probably out of necessity, but certainly combined with inclination, the idea that knowledge is out there, it's available. If you can't buy the book you can always go to the public library, and steal the thing if necessary!

I had, fortunately, grown up in a culture where learning was very important. The Jewish immigrants to South Africa had brought this culture with them. This kind of culture never said, 'This sort of thing is nonsense.' So there was no stopping me. Of course my mother believed that if one could divert this learning to become a surgeon or a lawyer, that was even better. And she always said that while one should never marry a girl for her money, it's just as easy to fall in love with a rich girl as it is with a poor girl!

I believe that one *can* become totally self-motivated, because the world is out there and it's just available. I think that most small boys, and probably girls as well, have an intrinsic interest in nature. In fact, I've noticed this in my own grandchildren. They begin with an interest in seeds and in animals swimming around and in looking at things with a magnifying glass. And I think that it's the formal teaching that destroys this.

I decided to become a scientist because I thought it was something you could actually do. I thought biology was important and it had this attraction. I didn't think I was clever enough to be a mathematician. And I found that physics, at least as it was taught to me, had gotten away from nature. It was all about pendulums and things like that!"

The South African higher education system was modelled on that in England, so it was possible for a bright student to go directly from secondary school (high school) to a professional course at university – for law, medicine or engineering for example. Parental ambitions for him to become a doctor suited Brenner reasonably well for the moment. His parents could not afford to give him a university education pursuing a degree in biology, and a town scholarship (bursary) to study medicine was the only option. Brenner was awarded a bursary of £60 a year to study medicine at the University of the Witwatersrand in Johannesburg. The bursary covered his fees, but nothing else. He entered the university in 1942 at the age of 14, making him three-to-four years younger than his classmates.

"My parents couldn't afford for me to live in Johannesburg, so I commuted every day from Germiston. That meant getting up at about a quarter to six, cycling to the station, catching the train to the Johannesburg station and then walking to the University, and doing this again at night in reverse. Being one of the poorer people in town I was offered this job that allowed me to earn sixpence a day [about five cents in US currency] for coming to the synagogue every morning – which was actually on the way to the train station – and being present for people to say prayers for the dead – *kaddish* – which they had to do on the anniversary of the death of a loved one, and for which they needed ten men over the age of thirteen. So I spent quite a lot of time being the 'tenth man' at prayers for the dead. I must say that I don't go to funerals now – I had enough of funerals for about four years of my life as a professional mourner. Of course I won't be able to avoid my own, but certainly not as a 'tenth man'!"

Once at the university, Brenner soon showed his intellectual colours. Like any medical student, he had to endure the tedium of some of the lectures, but his natural curiosity about biology soon led him to the research laboratory and experimentation.

"The first year of medicine you do botany, zoology, chemistry and physics, and so it's a pretty good scientific education. But the thing that stands out most from those days was that after classes I used to go to the research laboratories in the Botany Department. I met this very interesting lecturer in botany called Weinstein, who really taught me a lot of science. Every now and then I would help him in the lab. He showed me how chromatography worked. It was all done on kieselguhr. It involved the separation of carotenoid pigments by adsorption, which I recall being tremendously impressive. I love pigments. I love colour, because you can see it, you know. I've always been fascinated with dyes and the whole idea of interpreting what you can stain in cells and tissues. I really thought that this was going to be a powerful way to study biology.

The other person I came in contact with was a very great man called Edward Roux, and it was Edward Roux who taught me botany. He taught it as a living subject. It seems to me that Roux really communicated what would now be called plant physiology. Zoology was deathly. We had to dissect a dogfish and to learn things almost by rote. There was very little functional stuff.

My lecturer in chemistry was a man named [Manfred] Karnovsky who later went to Harvard. I once criticised him in class. He asked me a question and I told him that he didn't know what he was talking about! So, we still recall, he threw me out of the chemistry lecture theatre because I argued with him. Actually, I was right!

The second year of medical school was anatomy and physiology, and that was the beginning of a new kind of interest because I found physiology to be totally remarkable. What I found most interesting was biochemistry. We did a little bio-chemistry as part of the physiology course. However, I had discovered a book in the library called *Perspectives in Biochemistry*,[3] which was full of the most remark-able set of papers that I had ever read. It was this book that opened my eyes to the great richness that could come from the molecular explanation of living process-es. And I think that it was then, in about 1943, that I realised that one had to learn both chemistry and biology, and that there had to be a science that studied the function of cells – I didn't know what to call it at that time – which brought life and chemistry together in some strong sense.

In *Perspectives in Biochemistry*, I read a very interesting article by Scott Moncrieffe on the genetics of colour pigmentation in plants, which sort of closed the cycle on my own extractions of leaves and petals. This was the beginning of ideas about biochemical genetics and the first realisation, at least in my mind, about genes, which of course I didn't know about at all because we had no formal teaching in that subject. But I found being able to look down a microscope and actually see cells completely fascinating."

A pivotal point in Brenner's education at medical school was the realisation that if he continued uninterruptedly through the six-year medical curriculum he would grad-uate before he attained the age of 21, the minimum age required to become a regis-tered physician in South Africa. So the dilemma arose as to how to use the extra year. The University of the Witwatersrand Medical School offered an interesting option after completion of the second year. One could spend the third year doing a Bachelor of Science (BSc) degree in anatomy and physiology before returning to medical school to complete the Bachelor of Medicine and Surgery degrees.

Few medical students took advantage of this opportunity, but Brenner saw it as a way of broadening his scientific horizons and of solving his problem of graduating too

3. Needham J (Ed.). *Perspectives in Biochemistry* Cambridge: Cambridge University Press, 1937.
4. Needham J. *Biochemistry and Morphogenesis.* Cambridge: Cambridge University Press, 1942.

early. So, in 1945, he joined a small group in the BSc class at the medical school. This new environment turned out to be unexpectedly exciting.

"One suddenly realised that one was entering into real science, especially since in the Histology Department there were a number of people who had not only done a BSc degree, but had also done an Honours degree and in some cases a Masters degree. People were actually doing research. And so in that year I really began to do biological research. I became tremendously impressed by trying to work on cell physiology. I built my own Warburg manometer to measure the uptake of oxygen in tissues and this led me to think, 'Now I know what I want to do. I want to become a cell physiologist!' From the other side, from the histology side – and the two things eventually came together – I became very interested in looking at cells under the microscope. And I became very excited by the ability to do histo-chemistry – cytochemistry as it was called. I thought that somehow you have to have some synthesis between a system that you grind up and a system that you can actually look at.

There were a number of people who I found very, very stimulating. One of these was a senior lecturer in histology (and subsequently the Professor of Physiology) named Joseph Gillman. Joe was someone who exerted a great intellectual influence on a wide number of people. We used to spend hours and hours discussing the dif-ference between terms like 'evocation' and 'induction' in embryology. Joe and I read Needham's *Biochemistry and Morphogenesis*[4] at lunch time. We brought sand-wiches and sat down and read three or four pages aloud. It was quite talmudic!

Joe was a Marxist, so he believed in things like dialectical synthesis, which I never understood, but which essentially says that you can't learn anything from the mechanical disintegration of things. Later, I understood where all these ideas came from by reading Lenin's book *Materialism and Empiriocriticism.*[5] You may ask how one got to read something as esoteric as this. I have to tell you that one of the great things at that time in my education was a third subject that was compulsory for everybody doing a BSc degree at the University of the Witwatersrand. It was a course on the history and philosophy of science, taught by a man called Brian Farrell, who was a logical positivist. That became a very important thing for me. I was fascinated by reading about people who were not trained philosophers, but who became interested in science and examined the field – they were logical positivists of course – and developed an entire philosophy from it. So this sort of tinge in my attitude became quite important, and from that year onwards I spent quite a lot of time reading philosophy.

I started to read what the physicists had to say about philosophy, and in particular Max Born wrote a very interesting book at the time on causality in physics. I'd become introduced through this to all the problems of quantum mechanics. I read Einstein's more popular books on this, and so that was one of the things that led me on to an interest in these other aspects of science.

Of course, the war was still on and I became much more politically interested – and active – in South Africa. It's hard to describe! One was in this remote place with this provincial background which had no real connection to anything, and one was desperately trying to understand the twentieth century."

As a result of taking another year out to stay on and do an Honours degree, Brenner's bursary was suspended until he returned to his formal medical studies. To make ends

5.   Lenin VI. *Materialism and Empiriocriticism: Critical Comments on a Reactionary Philosophy.* Moscow: Progress Publishers, 1977. (First published 1909.)

meet he worked as a salaried technical assistant in the Department of Anatomy.

"I was paid *in lieu* of fees and I was also paid a small salary. I learnt how to fix and embed tissues for histology, and how to mount and stain tissue sections. It was then that I discovered the wonders of Pacini's fluid. Pacini's fluid has nothing to do with the opera! It was a preservative that consisted of 95% alcohol and 5% glycerine. Of course, glycerine is exactly what you need to cut the bite of the alcohol. I decided to have a taste of this stuff one day. This was on a Saturday afternoon and I woke up on the floor of the laboratory on the following Sunday morning still holding this measuring cylinder. I'd taken much more than just a taste, obviously!

After doing my BSc and the following Honours year, I decided to do a Master's degree – take yet another year out of medicine – and then maybe I could forget about ever going back to it! During this time I began to study genetics. I had become very interested in chromosomes and genes from looking at chromosomes in histology, and I decided that what I really needed to know more about was chromosomes and genes. During my Honours year I read a most influential book by Edmund B Wilson called *The Cell in Development and Heredity*.[6] In that book Wilson talked about chromosomes as the bearers of heredity, and I came to the conclusion that that's what I had to get stuck into – looking at chromosomes. So I decided to do cytogenetics.

Now there was nobody doing this anywhere in South Africa. In fact, I was the first person to do any cytogenetics at all. I learnt how do it by reading two books. One was a completely impenetrable book written by Cyril Darlington called

6.   Wilson EB. *The Cell in Development and Heredity*. New York: Johnson Reprint Corp, 1966. (First published 1896.)

Recent Advances in Cytogenetics, published, I think, in 1937.[7] The other was a little book by Darlington and LaCour called *The Handling of Chromosomes*,[8] which told you how to actually do this. There was this little animal in South Africa that everybody was interested in called *Elephantulus* – a little shrew - and I decided to determine the chromosome number of the shrew. So I learnt about cytogenetics and chromosomes and allocycly, and read widely from Darlington's book, and essentially that was my Masters thesis. It was entitled 'The chromosome complement of *Elephantulus*.' I published a paper on it as well,[9] and got it wrong because I got half the number of chromosomes – I was working with haploid cells from the testis. Of course that was an acceptable mistake in those days!

A friend and colleague called Harold Daitz really taught me the importance of asking questions in science. We spent hours (and this also became my love) sitting around in the lab until all hours of the night just talking science. It's something my mother never understood – and I don't think my wife has yet understood it."

Brenner's enforced study of anatomy, as a routine part of his medical studies, led to a lifelong interest in palaeontology, for the Department of Anatomy at the University of the Witwatersrand was led by one of the most distinguished anatomists and palaeontologists of the day, Raymond Arthur Dart. Dart, an expatriate Australian, propelled himself to academic fame (and more than a little controversy), following his discovery of an early hominid fossil skull, the famous Australopithecus africanus, *or Taung child as it was called, after the little South African town near which the*

---

7.   The actual title is *Recent Advances in Cytology*. London: Churchill, 1932.
8.   A fourth, revised, edition of this book was published in London in 1962 by G Allen and Unwin.
9.   Brenner S. **Multipolar meiosis in *Elephantulus***. *Nature* 1952; **164**:495–498.

fossil was unearthed. Dart was an extraordinarily charismatic individual. His personality was not lost on a single medical student who encountered his sudden entries into the anatomy dissection hall, or his spellbinding lectures on embryology, anatomy and, especially, anthropology.

"Dart had become famous throughout the world for the discovery of *Australopithecus*. And there was also the equally famous Robert Broom, who had started to excavate caves at Sterkfontein and Kromdraai just outside Johannesburg, and who discovered the famous Sterkfontein skull. While students, we went with Broom on expeditions to Sterkfontein and I was led to a very deep and serious interest in archaeology and palaeontology. It echoed something about my interest in nature, and brought me directly into contact with problems in evolution.

We would go to Sterkfontein for an entire weekend, and dig in the caves or sort rubble all day. And we played poker all night! We played poker using sheets of toilet paper as scrip. There was this hysterical evening once. Everyone knew about the Sterkfontein skull of course. Well, one morning at about 2am I achieved what I called the 'Sterkfontein hand'. It was a royal flush! It's the first and only time I did this, and I cleaned them all out of their toilet paper scrip. The only thing I ever discovered from this sort of excavation was in fact this 'Sterkfontein hand', which was a royal flush in hearts. I'll never forget that! In fact we woke everybody to show them this great discovery."

During the year that Brenner was completing his Master of Science degree, the distinguished English anatomist Sir Wilford LeGros Clark, Professor of Anatomy at Oxford University, visited the medical school in Johannesburg as a guest of Dart. Harold Daitz had joined LeGros Clark's department at Oxford as a research fellow the year before, and Brenner received a similar invitation directly from the great man himself. He was sorely tempted. Torn between his deepening interest in cell physiology, especially in genes and chromosomes, and his continuing fascination with palaeontology, he sought council from his mentor Dart, now Dean of the Medical School.

"Dart said to me, 'It sounds to me that what you're most interested in would be called biochemistry. But there are no jobs for people in biochemistry unless you are in a medical school. So what I advise you to do is go back and finish medicine and then become a biochemist.' I believe that I am the only person who graduated from medical school and had never seen a patient until his final examinations. I simply never went to the wards."

On the occasions when he did present himself at the wards, Brenner was frequently provocative. In his column for the journal Current Biology, *Brenner recently recalled:*

"I did not like clinical medicine. In fact I was thrown out of surgery ward rounds when a pompous statement that 'surgery is an exact science like chemistry or physics,' by a perfectly spherical thoracic surgeon, induced in me an outburst of hysterical laughter."

The South African system for graduation in all clinical subjects required that students examine patients in the presence of a Professor and be graded on the accuracy of the examination – and especially the diagnosis. Brenner was instructed to examine a particular patient's breath and report back with his diagnosis. The individual was a diabetic and Brenner was expected to make this diagnosis instantly by detecting the acetone quality of the patient's breath.

"I failed my medicine examination because I was asked to smell this patient's breath and (correctly) diagnosed Maclean's toothpaste, when I should have diagnosed acetone!"

This little incident cost Brenner an extra six months of study in order to obtain his medical degree. On the other hand, remarkably, he was at the top of his class in obstetrics and gynaecology.

"This was simply because you had to do this subject in residence in a maternity hospital, from which you could not escape. I was sent to a black hospital in Durban, South Africa. It was on the docks, and four of us had rooms in this hotel where amoebic dysentery was the mildest disease you could catch! The rest of the hotel, as far as I could work out, was taken by 'ladies' who entertained the sailors from the ships. Well, there was absolutely nothing to do except learn how to deliver babies and study obstetrics and gynaecology. So, since I had to do it, I managed to do it extremely well. I learnt a lot about life being stuck out there then!"

Brenner's scientific career was also continuing.

"One of the papers that I published during this time involved synthesising a lot of dyes, because I was interested in supravital staining of mitochondria. I read a paper that showed that Claude's 'microsomal particles' were the same as what the histologists were calling 'chromidial substance' (or 'ergastoplasm'), which had to do with protein synthesis. Claude[10] had fractionated cells in an ultracentrifuge, and showed that the particles came to occupy a certain band and that they

---

10. Albert Claude (1899–1983). Belgian cell biologist who was awarded the Nobel Prize for Physiology or Medicine in 1974 jointly with Christian de Duve and George Palade, for their discoveries concerning the structure and organisation of the cell.

contained nucleic acid [ribonucleic acid, RNA]. They, of course, are the ribosomes as we now know them – the seat of protein synthesis. Histologists had stained the chromidial substance or ergastoplasm with dyes, of which the most famous was methyl-green pyronin, which stained ribonucleic acid. But the issue was how could you prove that it was really the ribosomes that were being stained? The microsomal particles are submicroscopic, so you couldn't really see them. There were no ultracentrifuges in the medical school. So I took pieces of liver, put them in an air-driven turbine centrifuge and spun them at high velocity. I then cut sections of the liver and stained them. Each cell behaved like a little ultracentrifuge tube and the stained ergastoplasm sedimented to the same level that it did in a test-tube – above the glycogen band, or whatever. I was very proud of this experiment and I would say that this was my first connection with what one would call modern molecular biology, modern cell biology. Using new and different techniques to ask what things are going on in the cell.

Eventually I reached a point during the course of my sort of dual career as a reluctant medical student and a practicing scientist, and later on even a lecturer in physiology and a tutor all at the same time, when I came to the conclusion that I had to go abroad. And of course, after the war many people did. I had turned down this offer from LeGros Clark to go to Oxford. Then, in about 1948, Conrad Waddington came out to South Africa and a friend and I were asked to sort of look after him. Waddington was a great embryologist of the old school and he remained a friend for life. He told me about Cambridge and all the interesting things that were going on in biochemistry there. He had just moved to Edinburgh and said that of course I could come to Edinburgh if I wished. But I wanted to go to Cambridge. That's where the biochemistry was. So I wrote to AC Chibnall who was then a Professor at Cambridge, but I never got a reply. In the meantime I told the Principal of the University of the Witwatersrand, Humphrey Raikes – a great man who had been a physical chemist at Oxford – the sort of thing I wanted to do. And he told me about Sir Cyril Hinshelwood, who was Professor of Physical Chemistry at Oxford and who had written a book called *The Chemical Kinetics of the Bacterial Cell*.[11]

As a naïve young man I was very active in hunting around for those sciences that I thought could stand me in good stead for the future, which is a ludicrous activity you know. You say, 'Well, I think that topology is going to give one the big breakthrough', so you learn topology! And I had been through things like rheology – I had a great passion for rheology – and I knew everything about thixotropy and rheopexy, because I thought that trying to find out all about the physical chemistry of cytoplasm wasn't a bad idea. Anyway, I applied to Hinshelwood and was accepted. I read his book, which was full of equations. It didn't say too much about the stuff that was going on in his lab. In the meantime, I won a Royal Commissions for the Exhibition of 1851 Scholarship. There was only one scholarship a year for South Africa and I got it, and that took me to Oxford."

11. Hinshelwood C. *The Chemical Kinetics of the Bacterial Cell*. Oxford: Clarendon Press, 1946.

2
Seeing DNA

"Coming to Oxford was a great surprise in many ways. I had an image of England
that was completely distorted. As the boat docked at Southampton on a very cold
winter morning I looked out and everything was much smaller than I had imag-
ined it to be. Of course coming from South Africa, where distances are enormous,
the whole idea that places that were considered to be far away were only 30 miles
apart came as a surprise. And arriving at Oxford that day was a shock in a different way, because I learned of the death of my good friend and colleague
Harold Daitz that very day. I went directly to his flat to see him and was told by
his wife that he had died of a heart attack the week before – I hadn't known. This
was a terrible blow, because I had all sorts of ideas of how great it would be for
us to do science together at Oxford. However, I settled down and got myself digs
in Herne Road. There was still post-war food rationing in England, which of

course I didn't understand at all. I had to give my landlady all my points for meat so that I could eat breakfast there!

Hinshelwood was working on drug resistance in bacteria. He had written to me and said he'd like me to work on bacteriophage resistance to show that this phenomenon is an adaptation and not a mutation. I discovered a little book called *Viruses*, which was from a symposium held at Cal Tech in 1950. It's a remarkable book. I read avidly about phage in it and got very excited. This was the beginning of the phage ideas – stuff that was going to become clear in the next twenty years! So I started to work on bacteriophage and to read more about them.

Hinshelwood wanted me to work on phage resistance because he was a great believer at the time that bacteria adapted to certain situations and that what was inherited was in fact the adapted state. He didn't believe in mutations! He said that strictly speaking the evidence didn't support the idea that mutants existed! That was his thing! He was very controversial!

So I started working on bacteriophage resistance in a physical chemistry laboratory which was totally unequipped to do any biological work. We were given a pressure cooker and thirty glass petri dishes and some pipettes. You had to pour your own petri dishes and plug your own pipettes and sterilise them in an oven. Each experiment was a major logistical effort. Amongst other experiments that I did for my PhD thesis was a repetition of the famous Luria–Delbrück fluctuation experiments[1] that proved the existence of spontaneous mutations. I think I'm the

---

1. Experiments carried out by Max Delbrück and Salvador Luria (see footnote 6), which proved that phage-resistance in bacteria was due to mutation. These experiments were the foundation of the field of phage genetics.

only person in the world who repeated those experiments. I did this because Hinshelwood didn't believe them. But this got me deeply into the whole area of genetics and mutations."

Brenner was, in fact, very keen to work on a phenomenon called phage lysogeny. When some bacteriophage infect a bacterial cell they can exist in one of two states. In one state, they replicate, generating many phage particles before causing the cell to rupture (lyse) and spill out new phage. Alternatively, the phage genome sometimes integrates itself into the bacterial DNA and remains dormant there – the lysogenic state. Such dormant phage can switch back to the lytic state.

"I wanted to work on phage lysogeny because I thought that Hinshelwoodian theories could explain the switch between the lysogenic state of the phage and the lytic state of the phage. But Hinshelwood wanted to explain phage resistance. I tried to make him understand the fundamental difference between phage resistance during lysogeny [a state in which a bacterium is resistant because it is *immune* to infection by another phage] and phage resistance because of a bacterial mutation. In the end I said to him, 'Professor, in science as in life, it is important to distinguish between chastity and impotence: the outcome is the same but the reasons are fundamentally different.' Mutation says, 'You are bacteriophage-resistant because you have lost a receptor to bind the bacteriophage'. That is impotence! The other [lysogeny] is you choose to be chaste. It was absolutely unheard of that one would actually challenge the Professor in this way because we were still very much in the days where the *Herr Geheimrat*[2] was right at the top. Actually, I got on extremely well with Hinshelwood. He was someone who, if you could show him

2.   Private counsellor.

a good experiment, that would convince him. And at the end of the day he was willing to think that some things were in fact due to mutations!

I took full advantage of Oxford. For example, I had to get my phages from across the road in the Pathology Department, where I met some people who were working with Sir Paul Fildes. Fildes was a member of the old school of microbiologists who came to work every morning in a bowler hat and striped trousers. And I got to know people in the Biochemistry Department because I had to learn about bacteria, and in the Department of Organic Chemistry. In fact I got hold of a bench and was doing experiments there. One morning Sir Robert Robinson[3] swept in and started asking me questions about what I was working on. Of course I couldn't explain to him that I was an intruder! Apparently about a week later he asked where this interesting person had gone, because I'd done my work and disappeared!

At Oxford, scientists were regarded as second-class citizens and of course colonials were in the second division of the second class. So one's social life was quite restrained and had nothing to do with the University. I spent two years at Oxford, but being (a) a scientist and (b) a colonial I never really participated in the Oxford scene. A sort of postgraduate club called Halifax House had been set up in Oxford for the benefit of scientists. It was just across the road from the physical chemistry laboratory where I worked, and it was there that I met Jack Dunitz. Jack was a crystallographer, and he had been at Cal Tech until he returned to Oxford to work in Dorothy Hodgkin's laboratory. Jack knew Linus Pauling,[4] and Jack and I had

---

3. Sir Robert Robinson (1886–1975). British organic chemist, Nobel Laureate for Chemistry in 1947. At this time he was Waynflete Professor of Chemistry at Oxford.

many discussions, including ideas about DNA and how to determine the structure of DNA. Which was just complete nonsense I should say, because *my* idea was that you could do it by binding dyes to DNA and then look at the ultraviolet dichroism. And I thought you might be able to crystallise DNA with a dye in it. Through Jack I also met Leslie Orgel, who was a theoretical chemist at Oxford. We started a little group, in which I talked to them about genetics and of course I learnt a lot about structure from them. It was through Jack that I heard about Francis Crick in about November of 1952, and of his ideas of helical diffraction, which lead to the interpretation of X-ray structure."

Another person Brenner met through Jack Dunitz was Jerry Donohue, an American crystallographer who shared an office with Jim Watson and Francis Crick at the Cavendish Laboratories in Cambridge. In the final stages of determining the structure of DNA, the main problem was the 'base-pairing problem' – how did the bases adenine (A), guanine (G), cytosine (C) and thymine (T) projecting inwards from each strand fit together to form a regular structure?

"Watson had devised a model in which each base on one strand paired with its like on the other: A with A, G with G, and so on. However, this version was wrong, as was pointed out to him in no uncertain terms the following morning by Jerry Donahue. The reason it wouldn't work, said Donahue, was that Watson had the bases in what is called the *enol* form, rather than in their more likely *keto* form. The configuration of the *keto* and *enol* tautomers is slightly different, and hence, in theory, each could pair with a different base. Watson had chosen *enol* forms

---

4.   Linus Carl Pauling (1901–1994). American chemist, Nobel Laureate for Chemistry 1954 for his work on the nature of the chemical bond. Pauling had discovered the α-helix secondary structure in proteins and in the early 1950s, was also interested in the structure of DNA.

because all the chemistry texts showed the bases that way, which merely served to convince Donahue that the textbooks were wrong! When Watson reconfigured the bases in the *keto* form he hit upon the correct mode of base pairing, in which the purines A and G pair with the pyrimidines T and C, respectively. This was a turning point in solving the mystery of the structure of the DNA molecule.

An interesting story is that I was visited by Jerry Donahue in January of that year [1953] or some time around that, but certainly prior to the publication of the DNA structure. Jerry Donahue was a friend of Jack Dunitz and he came to visit me in the physical chemistry library at Oxford. We were talking about the DNA bases. I drew one of them and he said, 'Why do you draw it this way?' [in the *enol* configuration]. And I said to him, 'Because I've always drawn it this way. This is the way I've seen it in books that I have read.' Now this is quite interesting, because it was Jerry who pointed out to Watson and Crick that they were using the incorrect tautomer. I can't say there was any direct connection between my conversation with Donahue and his with Watson, but this might have provided a little input.

Of course the most important thing that happened then is that Jack Dunitz told me about all the developments with DNA in Cambridge because he was following it all. He told me that Francis Crick and Jim Watson had solved the structure of DNA, so we decided to go across to Cambridge to see it. This was in April of 1953. Jack and I and Leslie and another crystallographer went to Cambridge by car. It was a small car. It was very cold I remember, and the car wasn't heated. No one had heaters in cars then. We must have arrived in Cambridge in the late morning, at about 11 am or thereabouts. We went into the Austin wing of the Cavendish Laboratory. I went in with Jack and Leslie, into this room that was lined with brick, and there on the side I can remember very clearly was this small model with plates for the bases – the original model with everything screwed together. And I could see the double helix!

Francis was sitting there. This was the first time that I met him and of course he couldn't stop talking. He just went on and on and on, and it was very inspiring, you see. Of course at this stage neither of the two famous *Nature* papers[5] had yet appeared. The first paper was expected in a few weeks. They talked mainly about what eventually was in the second paper. Jim was at his desk in that room which I came to occupy later when I came to the Cavendish, and he was interspersing comments with Francis. So that's when I saw the DNA model for the first time, in the Cavendish, and that's when I saw that this was it. And in a flash you just knew that this was very fundamental. The curtain had been lifted and everything was now clear [as to] what to do. And I got tremendously excited by this.

I talked with Francis on that day. I was very impressed by the way he spoke and by his enthusiasm. Of course I'd heard about him as a crystallographer from Jack Dunitz and as the forerunner of the interpretation of helical diffraction. They talked about Bessel functions, you know. I didn't know a thing about Bessel functions! It sounded like an occasion where people I knew might get married! But Francis had to go somewhere and I got to talk more with Jim.

My initial impression of Jim Watson was of this rather eccentric, bright person who didn't pay as much attention to me as I would have liked, and who walked very rapidly with long strides – because we went for a walk. And someone who

5. Watson JD and Crick FHC. **A structure for deoxyribose nucleic acid.** *Nature* 1953; **171:**737–738. Watson JD and Crick FHC. **Genetical implications of the structure of deoxyribonucleic acid.** *Nature* 1953; **171:**964–967.

knew all the important people. You have to realise that this was my first meeting with someone who actually knew Delbrück and Luria.[6] I mean, I knew Luria's work; I was doing Luria–Delbrück experiments. And Jack Dunitz knew Pauling. It was a great thrill to meet people for the first time who knew other people who had experiments named after them.

In those days we used to jokingly contemplate what made people famous. In chemistry you had to have a piece of apparatus named after you. So today we remember Büchner by his funnel, Erlenmeyer by his flask and Liebig by his condenser! In mathematics you had to have a theory, or better still a lemma. Of course we wondered what you had to do in biology to have something named after you. Later I found out that you had to have a system – an *in vitro* system. So there was Nirenberg's system![7] This idea of having a system to do something was exemplified much later when I defined a rabbit as a system into which you put an antigen and from which you got an antibody!

Of course I was working on phage in Hinshelwood's laboratory, and Jim had worked on phage. Both of us had done extremely trivial work on bacteriophage. He did radiation sensitivity and I was doing absorption and mutation. But walking around with him I just knew that this was really the beginning of molecular biology. This was it, and all the rather simple ideas that I was fumbling through,

6. Max Delbrück (1906–1981). German theoretical physicist and phage geneticist, trained at the University of Göttingen and with Niels Bohr in Copenhagen. He came to the USA in the mid-1930s and switched to biology, settling at the California Institute of Technology, where he became the elder statesman of the molecular biological revolution. With Salvador Luria (1912–1991), he carried out the Luria–Delbrück fluctuation experiments which founded the field of phage genetics. Luria and Delbrück, with Alfred Hershey, received the Nobel Prize for Physiology or Medicine in 1969 for their work in phage genetics.
7. In the late 1960s, Marshall Nirenberg was one of the first to use cell-free protein synthesis successfully to assign individual codons to their corresponding amino acids.

you know, just reached immediate clarification. What we talked about mostly was not the structure itself but the biological implications, the stuff that appeared in the second *Nature* paper. The first paper just defined the structure and really had nothing to do with the explanation of mutation and replication and so on. There was a second paper which did that. The first paper was published side by side with the Wilkins–Franklin thing, you see. They put in this famous caveat phrase, 'It has not escaped our notice that the specific pairing we have postulated immediately suggests a possible copying mechanism for the genetic material.' Then they wrote a second paper which, by the way, nobody actually seems to have digested. Everybody compresses both. The second paper is the one that discusses DNA replication, discusses the problem of the unwinding of the chains, discusses DNA in terms of the mechanism of mutation and also raises all the questions of the code. And *that*, I think, was the most exciting thing – the biological consequences of the model.

Some people have said that Jim and Francis were lucky. Jim himself has said that he was lucky. Watson said, 'You need a bit of luck.' Well, you *do* need luck in science. Everybody can do with luck. Luck helps. I've always said for myself that I was lucky to be born at the right time, to have come to the right place, to have had my background, and to have met the right people at the right time. But it's very hard to say what these things are really about. Experimentally you'd have to run the whole DNA story again and remove the 'luck' factor and see if perhaps Jim would have turned out to be a second-rate birdwatcher [Watson had expressed a great interest in ornithology as an undergraduate], instead of a first-rate molecular biologist. Bad luck doesn't help anybody. But I think you could argue that good luck can make a poor scientist good. But what I really think is important is that topics reach a certain stage where they require someone to come and look at them from a completely different point of view."

New ideas were needed to solve the next big topic in molecular biology – the so-called 'coding problem'. This problem, in its widest aspects, addressed the nature of the correspondence between the gene – and by extension DNA – and the protein whose synthesis it specified.

The idea that a gene in some way directed the synthesis of a protein had been current since Beadle and Tatum's work on biochemical genetics in Neurospora *in the early 1940s, with their dictum 'one gene–one enzyme'. But even by the early 1950s, only a relatively few scientists (Brenner among them) were considering the revolutionary idea that DNA contained information – a 'genetic code' – that specified the order of amino acids in the protein. Indeed, the evidence that any given protein did have a fixed and constant sequence of amino acids was still largely circumstantial.*

However, for those prepared to recognise it, the idea that one linear sequence – the sequence of bases in DNA – could map directly onto another linear sequence – the sequence of amino acids in a protein – cut through the mass of purely biochemical data on the structure, function and synthesis of proteins to give a single central principle of great explanatory power.

"When I saw the DNA structure was also the first time that I recognised the real concept of the genetic code. That was a most remarkable thing for me. Biology had been three-dimensional. In fact a lot of people wanted it to be four-dimensional. But the idea that you could reduce it to one dimension was very powerful to me. That you could just have a linear sequence made the disentangling of everything so much easier to understand. It made copying DNA easy to understand. It made gene expression easy to understand. It made gene mapping easy to understand. And it made mutation easy to understand. In fact once you had this absolutely clear-cut conception, then in this very small evangelical sect we realised that everybody else was simply talking nonsense."

Brenner's interest in the genetic code dated back to a time well before his arrival in Oxford.

"I had actually started to grapple with the business of the genetic coding problem even before leaving South Africa. I had read a paper by Astbury in a symposium[8] in which he pointed out the relationship between the step size of nucleic acid – 3.3 angstrom units – and the step size of amino acids – 3.5 angstrom units. Astbury discussed the notion of the amino acids being determined by the nucleic acid. Dounce had already written coding papers.[9] And in fact, later I learnt that Cyril Hinshelwood himself had written a coding paper.

So before I went to Oxford I developed this idea that nucleic acid and amino acids were co-synthesised through aminoacyl nucleotide intermediates. I had this very naïve idea that the bases were joined to make a nucleic acid. Of course we knew the chemistry of DNA at that time, even though we had no idea about base-pairing. And I thought that at the same time as the nucleotides were joined, the amino acids were also joined to make a protein. It was an awfully crude idea, but in fact I had a mechanism which was very hot at that time, the notion of acylphosphate bonds – high-energy phosphate bonds. This seemed to me to fit pretty well,

8. Astbury WT. **X-ray studies of nucleic acids.** *Symp Soc Exp Biol* 1947; **1**:67–76.
9. Dounce AL. **Duplicating mechanism for peptide chain and nucleic acid synthesis.** *Enzymologia* 1952; **15**:251–253.

and I had great ideas that this is how proteins were made and specified."

The coding problem did not yield easily, however. In its various aspects, it was to occupy the thoughts and consume the efforts of the select group of molecular biologists, in which Brenner was soon to be included, for the next 15 years. As the historian Horace Judson described in his classic history of the period The Eighth Day of Creation:[10]

"The elucidation of the structure of DNA had been a concentration of forces, a siege, a conquest. The decade that followed was a story of dispersal and movement, of uncertain direction, wrong direction, multiple lines of work intersecting in fortunate encounters, and a way found at last through an unexpected break – as different from what went before as the Odyssey *from the* Iliad, *and yet with continuities of theme, style, character. After the structure of DNA was solved, biology opened up and opened out. The confusion I perceived was first, trivially my own, because the science, though not forbiddingly abstruse as some science is, was dauntingly intricate. Beyond that, though, was the confusion of extraordinary growth. In the crudest terms, no other science, not nuclear physics, has ever expanded as biology did in North America and Europe from the mid-fifties to the mid-sixties: new people, new and larger laboratories, more and ever-fuller meetings and journals and books; the dollar was constant and the biology was flexible, promising, and still cheap. Then there was another kind of opening up that was altogether more interesting: again and again, the smallest, most casual beginnings – a sceptical question asked in a Paris cafe, some specks seen on an electron micrograph, the idea struck off a sentence*

10. Judson HF: *The Eighth Day of Creation: Makers of the Revolution in Biology.* Harmondsworth: Penguin Books Ltd, 1995. [First published New York in 1979 by Simon & Schuster]

during a drive down from New England – have grown up into specialties that have since engrossed entire lifetimes in science, today command whole teams and laboratories, whose results fill volumes and are not ended." [Judson, p225–226, see footnote 10]

Brenner recognised that cracking the genetic code would be a truly formidable challenge. Aside from his pet theory about protein synthesis, his keen mind and sense for the 'right' questions had prepared him for his intellectual and experimental forays into the coding problem. The basic concept that genes might contain both the information to perfectly reproduce themselves – their genetic *function – and to encode a blueprint for protein synthesis – their* coding *function – was one that he had independently assimilated from an article by the Hungarian physicist John von Neumann.[11] Brenner had come upon this through his discussions with one of his close scientific colleagues and friends in South Africa, Seymour Papert, who went on to a distinguished career in computer science in the United States, at the Massachusetts Institute of Technology.*

"Papert was a very important influence on my life in South Africa. Seymour was a brilliant mathematician. He taught me mathematics and I taught him physiology. Thank God it wasn't the other way around! Among other things, Seymour and I wanted to know how the brain worked – you know, like a hobby on the side. After dinner we'd talk about central problems of the brain and how it worked! One of our discussions prompted me to get hold of a symposium entitled the *Hixon Symposium on Cerebral Mechanisms in Behavior*, which was held in Pasadena, California in 1948. The symposium was published in 1951, and in this

---

11. John von Neumann (1903–1957). Hungarian physicist and mathematician. von Neumann was interested in the logic and structure of artificial automata – computing machines – and how these might be exploited as models for aspects of biological behaviour, such as the function of the brain.

book was a very famous paper by John von Neumann[12], which few people have read.

The brilliant part of this paper in the *Hixon Symposium* is his description of what it takes to make a self-reproducing machine. von Neumann shows that you have to have a mechanism not only of copying the *machine*, but of copying the *information* that specifies the machine. So he divided the machine – the *automaton* as he called it – into three components: the functional part of the automaton; a decoding section which actually takes a tape, reads the instructions and builds the automaton; and a device that takes a copy of this tape and inserts it into the new automaton."

Brenner recognised that the paradigm of the self-reproducing coding machine embodied in von Neumann's description was fundamentally different from the description of the gene proposed by Erwin Schrödinger in his book What is Life?,*[13] in which Schrödinger hints at the coding properties of the gene.*

"Almost every one of my colleagues said that the book that influenced them most is *What is Life?* People would say, 'Were it not for Schrödinger, I'd be playing the violin and collecting money in the Underground!' I read the book myself at a very early stage and I must say that I don't recall getting anything out of it in terms of what other people claimed – namely that it introduced them to the concept of the

12. von Neumann's writings on cellular automata can be found in von Neumann JL: **The General and Logical Theory of Automata.** In *Collected Works*, Vol 5. Oxford: Pergamon Press, 1961:288–328.
13. Erwin Schrödinger (1887–1961). Austrian physicist. In the 1940s, Schrödinger published a popular book entitled *What is Life? – The Physical Aspect of the Living Cell.* Cambridge: Cambridge University Press, 1944, in which he speculated boldly on the structure of genes and on a code of life embodied in them. This short work was much admired by a small band of physicists interested in biology, and by more than a handful of biologists interested in genes, notably James Watson and Francis Crick.

gene as a molecule and so on. I knew all about genes and chromosomes, and this stuff seemed to me to be a bit amateur. I certainly didn't understand the entropy part of the argument. In fact, I wrote an inscription in my copy of *What is Life?* which must have reflected my impression of it at the time. It's from Faraday and it says, 'Let the imagination go, guarding it by judgement and principle, but holding it in and directing it by experiment.'

That has been very important to my approach, which is that you've got to really find out. It's the difference between having a correct theory and a true theory – that is, a theory that reflects reality. You've got to go back to nature and that's what this is saying.

Anyway, the key point is that Schrödinger says that the chromosomes contain the information to specify the future organism *and* the means to execute it. I have come to call this 'Schrödinger's fundamental error'. In describing the structure of the chromosome fibre as a code script he states that:

'The chromosome structures are at the same time instrumental in bringing about the development they foreshadow. They are code law and executive power, or to use another simile, they are the architect's plan and the builder's craft in one.' [Schrödinger, p20, see footnote 13]

What Schrödinger is saying here is that the chromosomes not only contain a description of the future organism, but also the means to implement the description, or program, as we might call it. And that is wrong! The chromosomes contain the information to specify the future organism and a *description* of the means to implement this, *but not the means themselves*. This logical difference was made crystal clear to me when I read the von Neumann article, because he very clearly distinguishes between the things that read the program and the program itself. In other words, the program has to build the machinery to execute itself. In fact, when he discusses the biological significance of his abstract theory, von Neumann, in a very modest way I think, goes on to say that:

'This automaton has some further attractive sides, which I shall not go into at this time at any length. For instance, it is quite clear that the instruction I is roughly effecting the functions of a gene. It is also clear that the copying mechanism B performs the fundamental act of reproduction, a duplication of the genetic material which is also clearly the fundamental operation in the multiplication of living cells. It is also clear to see how arbitrary alterations of the system E, and in particular of the tape I, can exhibit certain traits which appear in connection with mutation, which is lethality as a rule, but with a possibility of continuing reproduction with a modification of traits.' [von Neumann, p317–318, see footnote 12]

"Now this was published in 1951, and I read it a year later in 1952. But we know from later work that these ideas were first put forward by him in the late 1940s. I think that because of the cultural differences between most biologists on the one hand, and physicists and mathematicians on the other, it had absolutely no impact at all. Of course I wasn't smart enough to really see then that this is what DNA and the genetic code was all about. And it is one of the ironies of this entire field that were you to write a history of ideas in the whole of DNA, simply from the documented information as it exists in the literature – that is, a kind of Hegelian history of ideas – you would certainly say that Watson and Crick depended on von Neumann, because von Neumann essentially tells you how it's done. But of course no one knew anything about the other. It's a great paradox to

me that in fact this connection was not seen. Of course, all this leads to a real dis-
trust about what historians of science say, especially those of the history of ideas.

Most fields start by struggling through from experimental confusion to early theoretical self-delusion and finally to the great generality. The coding field, in my
view, starts the other way round. It begins with a total abstract generality, namely Gödel's hypothesis, or the Turing machine, and then it takes fifty years to
descend into banality. So von Neumann and Watson and Crick cross each other
in 1953 – one on the way down and the other on the way up. It was never put
together. I didn't put it together then, but I did a little bit later, because the
moment I saw the DNA molecule I knew it!

So the concept of information as distinct from matter certainly crystallised for me
during this period prior to my leaving South Africa for Oxford, through reading
von Neumann, and from my contacts with Seymour Papert. I realised the idea
that the genes have to carry information and I knew that there was no explanation of that.

I had this notion that you synthesised DNA – nucleic acid – and protein together.
So to me this idea of one-dimensional sequences was okay, and of course I was
very much intrigued by the von Neumann thing. His tapes that instruct the
automaton are one-dimensional sequences. And so all of this, this whole idea of
the embodying of information in the DNA, is an important and fundamental
breakthrough in my opinion. And to see that, and to be able to just get away from
the problem of the details of the mechanism was important. You see, at that time
all the biochemists of the world were preoccupied about where you get the energy to make proteins. We had to spend weeks, months, saying, 'Don't worry about

the energy. Energy will look after itself.' The important thing is how do you get everything to be specified in the correct order. The genetic code is the thing!

This was an extraordinarily important and fundamental divergence from anything else in biology – a total discontinuity. At least that was the way that I saw it. And of course this way of thinking crystallised the problems one had to solve in a very clear-cut way, because now they were not vague problems that you just asked rhetorical questions about. You could actually sit down and say 'If I had a gene that I could do the fine structure on, and if I had a protein that I could sequence, then I could show whether or not the gene and the protein are co-linear.'

Another interesting thing that emerged for me at the time that I first saw the DNA structure is that many people might have said, 'You've got to unwind the chains to be able to copy the structure, and that looks impossible.' And they might have eliminated the Watson–Crick structure on the grounds that the chains were not parallel, but were intertwined. That's the first time that it dawned on me that if the impulse of a theory is very strong, you need to have what I later called a 'don't worry hypothesis'. A 'don't worry hypothesis' is very important in biology. It is there to provide one with any plausible way that something can be done so that you don't have to worry about it at that very moment. You know, you can just get on with the real thing. One plausible mechanism that we postulated for unwinding the two DNA strands – and I remember the conversation well – is that there will be enzymes to do it. Which of course there are. They're called DNA helicases.

And so this is the first of the many 'don't worry hypotheses' that we generated in the early days of molecular biology in order to lessen the constraints on theory. The trouble with a lot of biology is that it's very hard for theory to be that compelling that you are willing to ignore certain facts. In order to do this you have to have a hypothesis that will allow you not of course to ignore facts, but to deal with what seem to be difficulties later, rather than rejecting the hypothesis out of hand as being impossible. Many people said that it is inconceivable that a polypeptide would fold up by itself. 'You have to have separate genes for folding the proteins.' But you just say, 'Well look, don't worry about this. It will be resolved later. It's done with no hands! How else would you expect it to be done?'"

Once the structure of DNA had been solved, the coding problem could be posed in a more specific form. It was immediately recognised that the bases A, G, C and T must be letters in a code that somehow specified the twenty amino acids that make up all proteins. The coding problem essentially embraced two questions: what is the code, and how is it deciphered to dictate the order of amino acids in a protein? Obvious as these questions might seem now, at the time, those who set out to answer them were still very much on the fringe of mainstream biology.

"The [informational DNA] model wasn't really accepted at first. At this stage, you had 'the establishment'. The establishment was all the biochemists, the big guys. People like Fritz Lipmann, [Feodor] Lynen – you know, all the people doing enzymology. The big person in the United Kingdom was Tommy Work, who was trying to understand protein synthesis. And I think that this whole idea that you could have a structure, which is just a theory, and that you could go from this theory to something that was biology, and that you could do all these things like genetics, was really unacceptable to them. Chargaff[14] said that molecular biologists were people who practiced biochemistry without a license! I can tell you, without saying who was involved, that even in 1958 the whole of DNA was still thought to be a flash in the pan – not right, you know, not known not proven. And to believe in this in 1953 and actually start to do experiments on it – this was something that was just implausible. Because it was neither genetics, nor was it biochemistry."

Notwithstanding widespread scepticism, evidence was accumulating on other fronts that helped move the fledgling topic of molecular biology forward.

"There is a club in Oxford called the Alembic Club, which was for the discussion of chemistry. And I can remember – I think it must have been either late 1953 or early 1954, but certainly while I was at Oxford – going to a lecture that was given by Fred Sanger[15] on the structure [the amino acid sequence] of insulin. He showed how he deduced the structure. I remember that he had a wonderful set of little blocks [representing amino acids] which he turned over to face the audience as he related the structure. And the thing that struck me, because protein structure was a totally impossible thing then, was that at the end of the lecture Sir Robert Robinson stood up and said, 'Doctor Sanger has made proteins part of chemistry. He's actually shown this remarkable fact that these things have a chemical structure in the form of the sequence of amino acids.' Until that time no one actually believed this. They all thought that proteins were polymers of amino acids just joined together according to their abundance. There's something called

14. Erwin Chargaff (born 1905). Austrian biochemist who emigrated to the United States in 1934 and worked at Columbia University on nucleic acid biochemistry. In 1950 he discovered the 'Chargaff ratios', the fact that the ratio of G to C and A to T is a constant, around one, in all species, although at the time he put forward no explanation for this finding. Watson and Crick used the idea of complementary base pairing, which they realized the Chargaff ratios confirmed, to build their model of DNA. Chargaff never considered molecular biology as a proper scientific discipline.

15. Frederick Sanger (born 1918). British biochemist and molecular biologist. Nobel Laureate for Chemistry in 1958 for his determination of the amino acid sequence of insulin, the first protein for which this had been done, and again in 1980 for his development of a technique for sequencing DNA.

the Bergman–Nieman hypothesis, which said that things occurred with a frequency according to their abundance. So that was the state of things, and I think that Sanger's work was a signal achievement in pushing the subject on. But of course that wasn't something that many people were doing, and Fred himself was a 'fringe person' in the Biochemistry Department at Cambridge.

This was the beginning of the fusion of genetics and biochemistry. It's worth just looking back to the mess that genetics was in at the turn of the century when it became an established science. Many people went into genetics simply because the problems they were working on were insoluble. The most important example is Thomas Hunt Morgan.[16] Morgan started life as an embryologist, but found embryology intractable. He wrote in his book *Regeneration*[17] that he in fact turned to genetics because he believed that this would give him a new entry to development. Most of the early geneticists did that. But by the beginning of World War II, after the first biochemical genetics was done in the fruit fly *Drosophila*, it became clear that it was extremely difficult to get any deeper by simply finding a mutant and what it does – that is, the purely descriptive level. So that's when people such as Beadle and Tatum[18] started to do biochemical genetics with *Neurospora*. This immediately attracted people like Boris Ephrussi[19] and Jacques Monod.[20] And by 1945 we *had* the idea that what genes do is control biochemical processes. But there it got stuck, and organismal genetics beyond that time went

---

16. Thomas Hunt Morgan (1866–1945). American embryologist and geneticist who founded the field of *Drosophila* genetics. Nobel Laureate for Physiology or Medicine 1933 for his discoveries concerning the role of the chromosomes in heredity.
17. Morgan TH: *Regeneration*. New York: Macmillan, 1901.
18. George W Beadle (1903–1989) and Edward L Tatum (1909–1975). American geneticists, Nobel Laureates for Physiology or Medicine in 1958 for their discovery that genes act by defining definite chemical events.

in the direction of population genetics. *Drosophila* was now in the hands of the population geneticists, and the only thing that was coming along in biochemical genetics was that of the micro-organisms.

So the fusion between genetics and biochemistry was totally absent then. But with the structure of the gene, and the implications of unravelling the code, you could actually begin to think of experiments. You could say, 'If this gene controls this enzyme, then it follows that if I get such and such a mutant, the following will happen.' And of course working with bacteriophage was particularly interesting.

Speaking of bacteriophages, someone once asked me what sort of statistical tests we did for significance in genetics. I remember that I said to him, 'We don't do any statistics.' But then I immediately followed, 'Oh, wait a minute. We plot our results on seven-cycle log paper and someone holds the sheet of paper at one end of the room and someone else is at the other end of the room and if you can see a difference it's significant!' The point is that the significance was obvious. Genetics is digital. It's all or none. We didn't have to make quantitative measurements. When you think about that it's very remarkable. If you're testing for a recombinant, you either got one or you didn't. Later on one could measure how much recombination one got. But in the beginning you could do everything by one and zero. You could do 'yes' or 'no' experiments. So you could do very remarkable experiments that you couldn't do in other subjects. We did experiments with pieces of paper and toothpicks. It was a marvellous period in which you could

19. Boris Ephrussi (1901–1979). Russian-born geneticist, worked in France and the United States on the genetics of *Drosophila* and other organisms.
20. Jacques Monod (1910–1976). French bacterial geneticist and molecular biologist. With André Lwoff and François Jacob, awarded the Nobel Prize for Physiology or Medicine in 1965 for their work on the genetic control of enzyme and virus synthesis.

make these mixtures [of bacteria and bacteriophages] and have a look if there were holes [plaques] or not on bacterial plates and deduce things about the molecular structure of organisms.

Well, after that first look at DNA, and meeting Jim Watson and Francis Crick, I decided that this is exactly what I must work on, and I went back to Oxford. I kept up a correspondence with Jim and he came to visit me later that year, on July 6th, 1953. I remember that because my young stepson, who was then seven, had a birthday party and of course Jim ate all the cake. He was a great lover of desserts!

At about this time I had to go back to South Africa. As far as I was concerned it looked as though come the end of my DPhil – that would have made it 1954 – I would have to return to South Africa, where a lectureship in the Department of Physiology had been arranged for me. But in the beginning of 1954, Milislav Demerec, who was then Director of the Cold Spring Harbor Laboratory,[21] and a very remarkable man, arrived in Oxford because he had connections with Hinshelwood. And he came to see me and he got very excited about what I was doing, which one must understand was very heretical then. Someone working on actual mutations! I realised this because he got up and closed the door of the lab before he started to talk to me. He said, 'Won't you come to Cold Spring Harbor?' He assured me that he could arrange for a Carnegie Corporation Travelling Fellowship for four or five months. So I agreed, and my family returned to South Africa and I went to America to spend the summer of 1954 in Cold Spring Harbor. And that was where I really got injected into the whole of modern science."

21. The Cold Spring Harbor Laboratory on Long Island, New York, USA.

3
America and
back again

Soon after he arrived at Cold Spring Harbor in the summer of 1954, Brenner made a visit to Woods Hole, Massachusetts,[1] another popular meeting place for the fledgling group of molecular biologists, where Jim Watson was teaching a summer course. Francis Crick was there and Brenner now got to know him well. Also there was George Gamow, the émigré Russian physicist and cosmologist. After the second DNA paper had been published in Nature *in 1953, Gamow, a total unknown in biology but a formidable theoretical physicist, wrote to Watson and Crick, volunteering a mechanism by which the code might work.*

In that second paper, Watson and Crick had proposed that "The precise sequence of the bases is the code that carries the genetical information." From the outset, there

---

1.   Woods Hole Marine Biological Laboratory, Woods Hole, Massachusetts, USA.

was a strong consensus that the genetic code was likely to be a triplet code. That is, three adjacent bases in the DNA would specify a particular amino acid. A codeword of just two bases would yield too few possibilities – only sixteen codewords (4^2) for the twenty amino acids – while codewords four bases long would yield far too many (4^4).

"But it was clear that the standard problem of the code was that there were sixty-four possible triplets in a non-overlapping three letter code [4^3], but there were only twenty naturally occurring amino acids. Gamow provided an explanation for this paradox. He suggested that overlapping triplets, that is triplets overlapping by two, would determine the code. He put this in a form which looked physical in the sense that there were diamond-shaped cavities in the DNA which covered the three bases, and he thought that the amino acids would fit directly into these cavities and hence be assembled into proteins. He showed that there was a way of arranging these cavities such that there were precisely twenty of them. And since this number came out to be the same as the number of natural amino acids, he thought the magic number had been reached – and that was the thing!

Crick immediately identified inaccuracies and problems with Gamow's code. Nonetheless, what Gamow did was to formulate the question of the code in a really serious manner. If you looked at the Gamow code you could actually show – and in fact Francis as far as I know was the first to do this – that the particular code Gamow proposed could *not* correspond to the amino acid sequences. But at the same time, it became realised that we could assign these triplets in any way we pleased. So the real problem was how could you show that any code was in fact not possible? A little later a computer specialist wrote a paper in which he stated that in order to eliminate all overlapping triplet codes we should have used a computer about a million times more powerful than the one we had and should have started working in the last days of the Roman Empire!

I'm a great believer in the power of ignorance. I think you can always know too much. I feel that one of the problems about being an experienced scientist in a particular field is that it can curtail creativity because you know too many reasons why something may not work. So I believe that it's people who come from the outside, who have not been entrained into the standard approach, who can see things a different way, who can take the new step.

Gamow didn't know anything about molecular structure. But he viewed this from the point of view of a physicist. And he could pose the problem in a form that no biochemist could pose, because that's not the way they thought about it. I believe that scientists are often mistaken about how we should best prepare ourselves for our heroic voyages of the future. The best way to prepare for a heroic voyage in science is just start. Don't equip yourself. I don't think that you can, so to speak, equip yourself, because things can basically take you from behind and surprise you. Someone once asked me what mathematics they needed in order to do biology. And I replied, 'The ability to count to twenty, that's all. There are twenty amino acids and four bases. You might have to go to sixty-four at some stage [there are sixty-four codewords in the genetic code], but you don't need much more than that.'"

George Gamow was a colourful character and stories about him abounded.

"His pronunciation you had to follow. He got mixed up between 'cytosine' and 'cysteine' and used the two terms interchangeably. So you really had to know the field to follow him. It used to be said that there were gentlemen with crew-cut hair and sober suits in the back of Gamow's audience, who were from the CIA or the National Security Council and who thought that *they* would crack this genetic code! Of course cracking the code became *the* thing.

It is interesting to see changes in the use of terms. At that time we thought of the code – and Francis has commented on this – as something like the Morse code, which was a table. It said S is dot, dot, dot, O is dash, dash, dash, and so on. That was a table of transformations, and we'd always thought of it that way. And of course the famous table of the genetic code is now done. Most people still talk about the complete apparatus of the genome as the genetic code of an organism. That is wrong. The code is the table of transformation."

The period at Woods Hole focused much intellectual effort on the coding problem, which had already been occupying Brenner for some time. Before he came to the United States, Brenner had devised a formal statistical proof that made the possibility of any kind of overlapping nucleotide triplet code extremely unlikely.

"If you have the first three letters of the gene correspond to an amino acid, so let us say ABB, and then you move one ahead and say BBC would correspond to the second [amino acid], you can see that the four letters [ABBC] correspond to a dipeptide – two amino acids. The number of possibilities for four letters [given that there are only four different nucleotides] is 256 [4^4], but the number of possible dipeptides is 400 [20^2]. This meant that if it was an overlapping triplet code of any form, we could not have all the dipeptides. So what you had to show to disprove this was that the present data would allow all dipeptides. Now of course there wasn't enough data to do this. However, there was enough data to do a Poisson analysis, which I did. I showed that if you saw the present [amino acid] sequences as a statistical sample of everything, it [an overlapping triplet code] was unlikely."

Brenner's stay at the Cold Spring Harbor Laboratory also proved rewarding. For it was here that he met Seymour Benzer, a future friend and scientific collaborator, who had already embarked on his classic experiments with the rII mutants of bacteriophage T4. Benzer had left his original calling as a solid-state physicist in 1949 to learn modern biology in Max Delbrück's laboratory at Cal Tech at Pasadena. After two years at Pasadena and a year at the Pasteur Institute in Paris, a leading centre of phage and bacterial genetics, Benzer was an accomplished phage geneticist.

Benzer's experiments focused on a particular gene, rII, in the T4 phage of the bacterium Escherichia coli. On his return to Purdue University in the autumn of 1953, Benzer had found a strain of E. coli that would not support the growth of phage that were mutant in the rII gene. Wild-type and mutant phage could thus easily be distinguished by whether they would form plaques or not on a carpet of E. coli growing in a petri dish.

Benzer could now readily identify new rII mutants, because a genetic cross between two different mutants would reconstitute a normal (wild-type) phage by recombination between the two mutant phage genomes. He knew from classical genetics that the frequency of these recombination events depended on the distance separating the two mutations in the gene. The greater the distance – that is, the further away in the linear DNA molecule two mutations were from each other, the higher the probability that a recombinational event would occur between them, thereby generating a normal viable phage.

Having discovered this way of generating and mapping the relative position of many different mutations in the rII gene, Benzer realised that by carrying out hundreds of crosses he could construct a very high-resolution mutational map of the gene, in which the position of mutations relative to one another was a direct function of the frequency of the crossover events between them. If he could make enough mutants, he should be able to 'saturate' the gene, that is, to make a mutant corresponding to each base-pair, and to prove by recombinational analysis that individual mutations could map with a resolution of adjacent base-pairs, the smallest possible physical distance between two mutations in DNA. With the phage rII system he could literally run the gene into the ground.

By the summer of 1954, when he and Brenner first met, Benzer had just embarked on this heroic effort.

"Seymour was there with his family and he had just completed the very first bits of analysis of the *rII* gene. As we once remarked, I was carrying around a whole lot of amino acid sequences and he was carrying these four or five mutants mapped in a single line. I immediately saw from what he had that the classic theory of the gene could now be broken.

It's important to understand what the classic theory of the gene was. The gene had been thought to be at once a unit of function, an integral unit of recombination, and an integral unit of mutation. What does this mean? This means that you could not recombine *within* genes, you could only recombine *between* genes. The old idea was that the genes were like beads on a string and you could recombine in the *string*, not in the *beads*. So the gene was indivisible as a unit of recombination. It was also indivisible as a unit of mutation.

Benzer was a remarkable person. Many of the scientists who came from physics and thought that they would find a new physics in biology just got lost in the metaphysical jungle. But Seymour had the ingenuity of being able to formulate experiments and to carry them out."

Within the next few years, thousands of genetic crosses were made, and Benzer refined the minimum unit of mutation to a single nucleotide, at least for short stretches of the rII gene.

"What Seymour did by showing that he could get hundreds of mutants in a gene, and that they could recombine, is to reduce the definition of the classical gene to an essential absurdity. Basically, he showed that physically the resolution he was getting on the DNA of this bacteriophage was equivalent to the resolution of base pairs in DNA."

During the course of the summer, the two men realised that Benzer's system provided the possibility of formally demonstrating that the nucleotide sequence of a gene and the amino acid sequence of the protein it encoded would have a precise linear correspondence – they would be 'co-linear'. A mutation at a single nucleotide in the DNA should be revealed by a corresponding change in the amino acid sequence. But the realisation of this experiment was delayed for several years. Brenner's fellowship was about to expire and the time to return to South Africa was drawing near. A few more eventful months in the United States remained. Brenner participated in the annual phage meeting at Cold Spring Harbor. Benzer had to leave because one of his children had taken ill and Brenner presented his rII mutant work for him.

"Of course, I got a lot of flak from people, for the simple reason that no one understood what this was all about. At this Cold Spring Harbor I met Leo Szilard.[2] He was the first person I met from really basic physics who'd become interested in biology after the War. I was very impressed by the fact that with every talk at the

Symposium that he didn't like, he'd get up and leave. He would stand by the door for a few seconds to give the speaker another chance. But if the talk didn't improve, as was usually the case, he would leave. Quite often I would join him on the balcony to talk. Szilard once told me that once he went into biology he could no longer enjoy a nice bath. When he was a physicist he could lie in the bath for three hours thinking about physics. But when he went into biology, no sooner did he get into the bath than he'd have to get out and look up another fact!"

After the Cold Spring Harbor meeting, Watson arranged for Brenner to spend a few weeks on the West Coast visiting Max Delbrück and others at Cal Tech, as well as some time at the Virus Laboratory at the University of California in Berkeley to work with Gunther Stent, a former postdoctoral fellow with Delbrück. Watson suggested that he and Brenner drive to California, stopping in Chicago to meet Watson's family, and in Urbana, Illinois, to meet Salvador Luria, now at the University of Illinois.

"We started at Cold Spring Harbor, and I have to tell you that Jim had just learned to drive and he had a Chevy convertible. I had spoken to people that he'd driven across the States from the West Coast who had quite a hair-raising trip with him. But he seemed all right. We spent a night at Yale with Jim's uncle, who was a professor of physics there, and then headed for Boston. We had no radio in the car, and unknown to us the famous hurricane Caroline struck the East Coast. We drove into Boston in an appalling storm and went to a house that wasn't furnished, where Ephrussi was going to be staying, and slept on the floor in sleeping bags.

2.   Leo Szilard (1898–1964). Hungarian-born nuclear physicist who had helped to initiate the United States atomic bomb project. After the World War II he turned to biology, and also helped to found the Pugwash conferences, a forum for campaigns for nuclear disarmament.

There was a terrible storm that night and I woke up to find the place half under water. I had never been in Boston before and it looked very bad. I woke up in the morning to this tremendous knocking on the door. The plumbers were trying to get in. Jim went on sleeping as they traipsed through the room. Eventually we got up and drove out for breakfast. The entire town was deserted. There was water everywhere: I'd never seen rain like this. We seemed to be the only people driving around. I asked Jim, 'Isn't this a bad storm?' And he replied, 'No, we get them this way here.' We drove past a church and I noticed that the entire steeple had fallen into the ground. My eyes opened wide and I said to Jim, 'Well then, did you see that?' It was only later when we went to the lab [at Harvard where Watson had just accepted a faculty position] and discovered everyone huddled around the radio, that we found out that we were driving as the eye of the storm passed over Cambridge.

We stayed with Ernst Mayr for a couple of days because Jim had interests in one of Ernst Mayr's daughters! Then we went west to Chicago where I stayed a few days with Jim at his family home and met his family, and then on to Urbana, Illinois, where we stopped for an afternoon and met Luria and Ed Lennox and all the people who were at Urbana. While driving through a small town in Kansas where they had a ridiculous speed limit, like 25 feet an hour, I noticed this policeman tailing us. I was driving and I said to Jim, 'What do we do?' And he replied 'Just drive.' Just as we reached the Kansas–Colorado border, the policeman stopped us and said, 'You went through a traffic light. Get out of the car'. I replied, 'I could have; I don't think I did, but if I did I'm terribly sorry.' This was a Friday I remember and Jim kept saying to me through the side of his mouth, 'Don't argue with him because he'll put us in jail and there'll be no judge 'till

Monday and we'll have to spend the weekend in jail!' He asked to see my driver's license and established that Jim owned the car. Then he went to look at the registration and he asked Jim, 'Are you Mr. Dewey?' Because Jim's middle name is Dewey – James Dewey Watson. He was named by his father after the philosopher Dewey, at Chicago. Jim didn't like the name and of course he certainly didn't like the policeman calling him Mr. Dewey! I could see Jim getting very het up, so I kept on saying to him through the side of my mouth, 'Don't talk back to him or we'll be in jail for the weekend!'

Having travelled a lot in South Africa through deserts and mountains, this was just fabulous scenery: the Rockies and the deserts. And it was hilarious because before we went through Monument Valley Jim said, 'You can't get anything for 200 miles', or whatever it was. He gave me this picture of us disappearing there – only our bleached bones in the desert. And while Jim was writing postcards to all his friends saying, 'Farewell, we're about to embark through this desert', I, who had travelled through deserts many times, was getting properly equipped! I bought an extra fan belt and I actually bought water. I mean, Jim was buying ice cream, and I bought canisters of water! I also bought a jar of butter, I believe it was. Something that you could use on a piece of a shirt to make a spare diaphragm for the fuel pump. I had once been stuck with a collapsed fuel pump in the desert in South Africa and of course, once that happens you've had it! We had made a makeshift diaphragm out of a shirt smeared with Vaseline. But of course all of this was just ridiculous. The desert was highly populated. There were Atomic Energy Commission trucks everywhere and you could buy a Coke every now and then. So the great episode of landing up as a pile of bleached bones never materialised!

We talked a lot about science during the long drive across the United States. But at that stage everything was at the beginning and everything was plans. And plans can be very unsatisfying, you know. We once had a Swedish biochemist visiting us and I said to him, 'What do you do in Sweden?' He answered, 'Ah, in summer the girls, the most beautiful girls in the world.' So I said, 'What do you do for the other 46 weeks?' And he replied, 'We plan for the summer!' So plans are really very unsatisfying.

Arriving at Cal Tech again brought me in direct contact with the phage group – the 'phage church' – at which I met many people who became life-long friends. I spent eight weeks working with Gunther Stent in Berkeley.

And then, of course, the time came for me to go back [to South Africa]. But by this time I knew exactly what I wanted to do. We would investigate the correlation between genes and proteins by finding a gene on which we could do fine-structure mapping, and then [identifying] its corresponding protein, on which we could do chemical sequencing. The first question would be to prove co-linearity. Namely, that the mutations occurred in the gene in the same order that they were present in the proteins. This plan was inspired by work by Vernon Ingram, who actually showed that sickle-cell haemoglobin (which Linus Pauling had showed involved a chemical change in the protein) was a single amino acid change, the conversion of a glutamic acid to a lysine.[3] Ingram had invented a fingerprinting method to show this. So we were going to fuse these two technologies in order to investigate the relation between genes and proteins. Of course, at that stage this

---

3.   Ingram VM. **A specific chemical difference between the globins of normal human and sickle-cell anaemia haemoglobin.** *Nature* 1956; **178:**792–794.

was all enormously difficult to actually do. You had to have large amounts of protein to do this sort of thing.

But we knew that in order to do this we would either have to isolate the protein of the *rII* gene (which we actually never succeeded in doing), or we would have to find another gene which specified something else in the phage. There were some phages that were not absorbed to the bacteria unless tryptophan was present, and I thought it should be possible to get mutants for this.

So I returned to South Africa in December of 1954 with the idea that I would start to work on the genetics of cofactor requirement in order to prepare the way for a full gene–protein analysis. This was something I knew I could do in South Africa. I was extremely depressed when I left America, because at that time I thought I'd never see it again. I felt, you know, that this was the end of everything, but there were already conversations about my returning.

On the way back to South Africa, I went to England and talked to Francis. We had discussions on degenerate coding [the idea that the same amino acid might be specified by more than one codeword] and other things, and there we had the idea that I would come and join them in the Cavendish. Because we were talking the same language, you know.

I set up a laboratory in the Physiology Department at the University of the Witwatersrand. I had plenty of space there and I got a grant from a South African cancer organisation to do phage cofactor genetics. I did all of that there. I'm very proud of that, because I actually did get recombinants for cofactor mutants. I developed methods for doing this and I published it. I was also proud because when I sent the manuscript to Max Delbrück before I published it, he called together a seminar to discuss this work.

I also continued to work on my coding theory. In fact, by late 1954 I'd thought of a trick to actually prove that all overlapping triplet codes were impossible. I wrote an RNA Tie Club thing [this club is explained in Chapter 4] from South Africa that was circulated. Gamow thought that it was important and got it published in the *Proceedings of the National Academy of Sciences*. It was a theoretical paper and it was entitled 'On the impossibility of all overlapping triplet codes'.[4] I'm proud of that paper because that was just really spurred by just knowing how to divide by four! I continued to think about the coding problem at a theoretical level. But at about this time, Francis had come to the conclusion that the code was degenerate and that we would not be able to deduce it from first principles. We would have to find out what it was.

Lots of people remained in South Africa, and some of them became quite important. But the testing ground, the personal testing ground, is at the centre. You've got to go to the metropolis – if I can call it that – and you've got to test yourself at the international level. Because otherwise you don't know whether you're any good or not. That's really what it was, and since at that time I believed that in South Africa the colour of my skin would always make me an outcast, because that's the way it looked at that time, I decided that I would do science. And that's why I went back to England. It was a conscious decision."

Brenner's keen intellect had been appreciated by those he had encountered in the United Kingdom and the United States, and job offers began to roll in – from the

---

4. Brenner S. **On the impossibility of all overlapping triplet codes in information transfer from nucleic acids to proteins.** *Proc Natl Acad Sci USA* 1957; **43**:687–694.

Medical Research Council (MRC) in England to work in the Cavendish Laboratory,
from Gunther Stent at Berkeley, and from Joshua Lederberg, then in Wisconsin. But
when the MRC offer came through, Brenner quickly made his decision to join the
Cavendish group. In December 1956, he once again docked at Southampton, this time
with three children and a three-year appointment beginning on the 1st of January
1957, at a salary of a thousand pounds a year. Brenner had corresponded extensive-
ly with Crick and the plans to go at the gene–protein problem were set.

"We would tackle this problem in bacteriophage, and a lab would be set up. Seymour Benzer and George Streisinger were going to join us. The phage laboratory had to be set up from scratch. There were no kitchens or anything, and our dish-washing facility was in our office. There were seven desks in this office shared with various crystallographers. We had one bench in a chemistry lab. There were wonderful episodes when we had to grow large amounts of phage in *E. coli.* And I conceived of the idea of growing them in a Hoover washing machine which opened from the top and had a pump that circulated everything. And I thought, 'You know, this is exactly what we need to grow large quantities of phage.' So I wrote to the Hoover company and they actually gave me a washing machine. But we could only use it one time because the medium corroded the aluminium and in fact the thing was totally useless."

As was his habit, Brenner soon expanded his research horizons, starting to examine
phage under the electron microscope. In those days electron microscopy was an eso-
teric discipline that required collaboration with specialists who extracted a very high
price for their collaboration. But after much trial and error, Brenner spotted an image
of the phage in the electron microscope that reminded him of the negative staining
used to visualise the micro-organism that causes syphilis – the spirochaete

Treponema pallidum – *under the light microscope.*

"I remembered from my medical studies that one put a drop of biological material on a slide and one then put the whole thing under India ink. And you could see the *Treponema* as [unstained] white objects transmitting the light swimming in this sea of ink. This is called negative staining and it was invented in the nineteenth century for the optical microscope.

This [Brenner's development of a method of negative staining for the electron microscope] took electron microscopy out of the hands of the elite and basically gave it to the people. It gave all the people working in virology a tool that they could use, and really wiped out the profession of electron microscopy in a biological laboratory, because anyone could do it. I think this was important because visualising phages and sub-phage particles under the microscope generated the ability to begin to think about macromolecular assemblies. And of course the molecular biology of the cell is really about how bunches of molecules get together and interact.

By the autumn of 1957, the phage laboratory was up and running, and Benzer and Streisinger arrived soon after. Seymour felt the cold very severely. He came in October and was so cold that he was ready to go home. But I dissuaded him. I used to come to his home and make fires for him to help him keep warm. Seymour's the only person I know who might walk around with a sweater in Death Valley when the temperature's 120[F]. He's always been cold! Benzer also liked to sleep very late. He's an owl. I have at various times in my career been an owl or a lark – and sometimes both – but Seymour liked to sleep late.

Time magazine called me that year because George Beadle had just won the Nobel

Prize. They called me from London and wanted to speak to Doctor Benzer, and I told them that Doctor Benzer was still asleep. So they asked whether I knew where to find Doctor Garrod. I said, 'Just hold on a moment, I'll look that up.' Now this was Archibald Garrod they were referring to. Garrod is considered by many to be the founder of modern biochemical genetics – the physician who worked on alkaptonuria as a hereditary biochemical defect. And of course he had long since died, and what I went to 'look up' was his obituary to find out where he was buried, you see. So I could give *Time* magazine directions to the Highgate Cemetery, where I thought they might be able to get him! In fact I told them, 'You're probably more likely to wake him up than you are Seymour Benzer!'

Food in England in those days was atrocious. You had a choice between a bad Chinese lunch and a terrible Chinese lunch. So Seymour, George and I, and Sewell Champe, a student that Seymour brought with him, decided to form a lunch club and cook for one another. The impulse to outdo each other became so great that in fact people would start cooking two days before the meeting. George in particular was a gourmet and once he went all the way to Yarmouth to get mussels, so that we could have *moules marinière*. Things started getting to the stage where we were spending more time on preparing grand lunches than anything else. But what happened is that Seymour killed it all one day when it was his turn to cook, and with a rather shy smile on his face he admitted that he had overslept, and produced four packets of fish and chips. That was the end of the lunch thing."

Progress on the co-linearity experiment kept stalling because of the gnawing problem, which in the end proved intractable, of identifying a target gene for which the corresponding protein could be isolated and analysed. Meanwhile, there was an interesting intellectual shift in the design of the co-linearity experiment, typical of Brenner's originality of thought.

"Seymour and I had this idea that if we could find a chemical reagent that we knew specifically changes one base to another – G to A for example – and you knew that this change resulted in a mutation in a particular amino acid, then if you looked to see what the amino acid change was, you might be able to work out the code. That was the dream! Of course we never got it done that way!

Well, we had all of these experiments going on at the same time and we had this wonderful group in that year. Seymour Benzer, George Streisinger and Mahlon Hoagland, who was working with Francis Crick [see Chapter 4], were all there. We struggled on with this gene–protein problem. People came and people went. And during this time there were all these sidelines going on – structural work on bacteriophage, negative staining by electron microscopy, the mutagenesis work, and so on. And we had the capacity to explore all of these things at once.

And of course there were now competitors in the field. Having formulated this programme of the co-linearity of the gene and its cognate protein many people said, 'Well we'll do this as well,' and one of them was Cyrus Levinthal and he decided that he would do it with the bacterial gene for alkaline phosphatase. And the other person who did it later on was Charles Yanofsky with a tryptophan biosynthesis gene. So what I learned from this, which is very important, is that we kept saying that you have to have a special system – bacteriophage – to prove this. But in fact, once you've formulated a question, if it's general enough you can solve it in any biological system. What you need to do is find which is the *best* system to experimentally solve the problem, and as long as it's general enough you will find the solution there.

The choice of an experimental object remains one of the most important things to do in biology and is, I think, one of the great ways to do innovative work. You have to say, 'Well, the diversity in the living world is so large, and since everything is connected in some way, let's find the *best* one.' I can remember that we thought that somewhere there must exist *the* perfect bacterium. This bacterium had 28% of its protein in one single polypeptide. The molecular weight of this protein is 16,000. It crystallises when you bubbled carbon dioxide through the extract. This bacterium also has all the capacities to do genetics at high resolution. So we said laughingly, 'Well, you know, maybe we should go and look for this thing!' I've always made sure that I follow the literature for things that look unusual, especially the microbiological literature, because there always might be something of interest.

It was now very clear that with the crystallography developing then – Max [Perutz][5] and John Kendrew[6] had started to solve myoglobin and haemoglobin – this unit, which had been called up to that point the Unit for the Molecular Structure of Biological Systems, couldn't last in the Cavendish, and that it would have to find a new home. Many things were explored. For example, at one time we explored the possibility that the physicists, that is the crystallography group, would stay in the Cavendish and that Francis and I and our group would go to the Genetics Department. Francis applied for the Chair in Genetics at Cambridge

5. Max Ferdinand Perutz (born 1914). Austrian-born chemist and protein crystallographer, working in Cambridge, UK, from 1936. Nobel Laureate for Chemistry in 1954, with John Kendrew, for his determination of the structure of haemoglobin by X-ray crystallography.
6. John Cowdery Kendrew (1917–1997). British protein crystallographer. Nobel Laureate for Chemistry 1954, with Max Perutz, for his determination of the structure of myoglobin by X-ray crystallography.

and was turned down. Francis Crick was not thought to know anything about genetics! Seymour tells a nice story about this. When Fred Sanger came to Purdue to give his insulin [protein sequencing] lecture, Seymour came up to him and said, 'Oh you're from Cambridge. Do you know Francis Crick?' To which Fred replied, 'Crick? Oh yes, he's the fellow who's rather keen on genes!' But Francis was not thought to know enough about genes, even if he was keen on them, to warrant being appointed a Professor at Cambridge.

We explored the possibilities of moving into the Chemistry Department. But that wouldn't work. Then the MRC said they'd make a building for us. So we tried to find a central site there, because in those days you wanted to be in the centre. People were in and out of each other's laboratories, and the pubs were around this area, and you could always meet people there, ranging from the Molteno Institute to the Biochemistry Department. So it was a real intellectual centre.

Eventually the MRC did fund and construct a new building in Cambridge called the Laboratory of Molecular Biology. That's the first sort of official use of the term 'molecular biology'. It comes from the 'Molecular Structure of Biological Systems'. And that's about the time that we founded the *Journal of Molecular Biology*."

It was in this environment that Brenner and Crick were to play a key part in deciphering the genetic code and the mechanisms by which it is translated.

4
Discovering
messenger RNA

When Brenner returned to Cambridge in 1956, his long and fruitful association with

Francis Crick began in earnest. This intellectual partnership had started when the

two men met at Woods Hole in the summer of 1954, and had been cemented by cor-

respondence while Brenner was in South Africa.

"When we all got together in Woods Hole is where the interaction became strong, because it became clear that the ideas one was talking about were the same, you see. And of course I have a long correspondence with Francis that goes back to after I returned to South Africa. Later we shared an office for twenty years and I had many, many conversations with him. Francis had a remarkable ability to crystallise questions in a particular way. I've always tried to materialise a question in the form of, 'Well, if it's like this how would you go about doing anything about it?' So I've always tried to think of some experiment, or where one might get hold of information to test this. Francis and I always had this kind of interaction.

The one thing that really characterised our conversations is that we never restrained ourselves in anything we said – even if it sounded completely stupid. We understood that just uttering something gets it out into the open and that someone else might pick up from that. There are people who will not say anything until they've got it all worked out. I think such people are missing the most important thrill about research – the social interaction, the companionship that comes from two people's minds playing on each other. And I think that's the most important thing. To say it, even if it's completely stupid!

I think that you can divide people into geometrists and algebraists. The algebraists are the people who sit down and write axioms and then proceed to deduce the answer. I can't do that. I can only think in terms of little diagrams. And Francis is very good at that as well: drawing little pictures and little diagrams of how things might interact. Another thing that I learnt from these interactions was to get the scale of everything right. Very early on we realised that the amount of DNA in a single bacterium is one millimetre long. And it's in a bacterium that is one micron in diameter. So the DNA has to be folded up a thousand times. So of course the pictures that you see of a bacterium with a little circle in it are ridiculous. Furthermore, when you think that most of the bacterium is full of ribosomes, the correct picture is not that ribosomes move along the messenger, but the messengers must be moving through the cell like a lot of hysterical snakes threading their way through the ribosomes. I've always thought of it as very good to get these pictures over. I feel that there's not enough done about this: people don't teach scales of anything and how molecules reach things. And Francis was good at that. That's one of the things we tried very hard to do; to stay imprisoned within the physical context of everything. And of course he is a very severe audience. You don't get away with things. You have to be thinking all the time, because he asks very penetrating questions. So there's a clarification that comes from that, which I think is very important in scientific interaction. And there were the sort of seminars we had; not just formal seminars and formal listening. We spent days and weeks just discussing things. Take the term 'nonsense' in the genetic code. There's all kinds of nonsense, you know. There's gibberish, there's nonsense, and so on, but to formulate what one meant by 'non-sense' in the genetic code took a long time to clarify.

I've always felt that the three things that came together to create the modern period of molecular biology were first of all Fred Sanger's proof that proteins have a chemical structure, which no one [had] believed – everybody thought they were statistical polymers, or just blobs; Seymour Benzer's work on the fine structure of the gene; and of course the Watson and Crick hypothesis. All of this was put together as the 'sequence hypothesis' by Francis in a paper,[1] which was much more important than the DNA paper.

You see, everybody knew that enzymes were functional things and that they had a complex structure. People actually thought that there were separate genes for folding the proteins – that there was separate machinery to do this. And Francis' real basic simplification was that there were two sequences: a one-dimensional sequence on the DNA which specified a one-dimensional sequence of amino acids in a polypeptide chain, and the one-dimensional sequence of amino acids in

---

1.   Crick FHC. **On protein synthesis.** *Symp Soc Exp Biol* 1958; **12:**139–140.

the polypeptide chain in turn specified how the protein folded up. And that's the fundamental thing. That really crystallised all the problems, all the issues, into the following question. How does the DNA structure map onto the amino acid sequence? That is, what is the genetic code? Of course there's also a subsidiary question, which is what is the mechanism of protein synthesis? But we could formulate an abstract question: what is the nature of the genetic code? And of course what the theoreticians wanted to do was solve it without hands."

The more practical side of the coding problem centred on how the information from DNA was transferred to protein. Were amino acids lined up directly on the DNA 'template' – an idea that was soon dismissed – or was there some intermediate? The idea that this intermediate was ribonucleic acid (RNA), the other nucleic acid in cells, was generally accepted among those working on the coding problem. However, how RNA might work and what its relation was to DNA on the one hand and to protein on the other was still obscure. Watson, now at Cal Tech, had decided to approach the problem by trying to determine the three-dimensional structure of RNA.

"At that stage, people like Jim Watson – and to a lesser extent Francis and people like Alex Rich[2] – believed that you would understand protein synthesis by doing [establishing] the structure of RNA. So they started to try and do for RNA what had been done for DNA. And of course they were completely wrong. It never worked out that way. But that was what was believed, and that is what Jim was trying to do at Cal Tech. I believed that we had to go from the genetics. To me that was the open door. Get genes, make mutants and study them."

2. Alexander Rich worked with Jim Watson on RNA structure at Cal Tech in the 1950s.

While at Woods Hole in the summer of 1954, Crick had talked with the French geneti-cist Boris Ephrussi. Crick related to Ephrussi the expectation that genes and proteins were co-linear, and described Brenner and Benzer's plans to prove this experimen-tally. Judson tells us that:

"Ephrussi took [Crick] aback by asking how he knew that amino acids were not put in their primary sequence by something in the cytoplasm. 'I don't think Boris neces-sarily believed it, but it was an idea he thought wasn't impossible', Crick said. Later that summer Crick took the next great imaginative leap. He invented a new piece of anatomy." [Judson, p280, see footnote 10 Chapter 2]

The "new piece of anatomy" that Crick deemed essential for protein synthesis was originally called the adaptor, *but eventually became known as transfer RNA (tRNA). Crick described this in his autobiography,* What Mad Pursuit: A Personal View of Scientific Discovery.[3]

"The main idea was that it was very difficult to consider how DNA or RNA, in any conceivable form, could provide a direct template for the side chains of the twenty standard amino acids. I therefore proposed a theory in which there were twenty adap-tors (one for each amino acid), together with twenty special enzymes. Each enzyme would join one particular amino acid to its own special adaptor. This combination would then diffuse to the RNA template. An adaptor molecule could fit in only those places on the nucleic acid template where it could form the necessary hydrogen bonds to hold it in place. Sitting there, it would have carried its amino acid to just the right place it was needed." [Crick, p96, see footnote 3]

3.   Crick FHC: *What Mad Pursuit: A Personal View of Scientific Discovery.* New York: Basic Books, 1988.

Crick formalised his hypothesis in a manuscript entitled 'On degenerative templates and the adaptor hypothesis'. This manuscript, which Crick referred to as his "most distinguished unpublished paper" [Crick, p96, see footnote 3], was distributed to all members of another 'magic circle' – the cryptically named RNA Tie Club. The RNA Tie Club was founded by the irrepressible George Gamow and consisted of scientists interested in the coding problem. The club was exclusive, with just one member for each amino acid found in proteins. There were hence only twenty members, all of whom were friends or colleagues of Gamow. Each member received a custom-made tie from a Los Angeles haberdasher, as well as a tie pin with his own amino acid spelled out. The tie pins were assigned alphabetically.

"Needless to say, Gamow was alanine! Francis was tryptophan, Leslie Orgel was tyrosine and I was valine, the last one alphabetically. There were also four honorary members who were called by the DNA bases. The club had a Chief Optimist – that was Jim Watson, and a Chief Pessimist – that was Francis. It was a typical Gamow thing.

Gamow had a job in Washington at George Washington University, but he was a consultant to the Los Alamos Laboratories. So he travelled west very frequently. One time he landed up in Chicago, which is where one had to change trains, and he realised that he had run out of money. So he went into this hotel to change a cheque. But his cheque was on the Falmouth bank in Woods Hole. He told them he was a Professor in Washington and that his name was Gamow. He even produced his Los Alamos security card as identification. The young man in the hotel was looking very suspiciously at this character with a strong Russian accent with a cheque drawn on a Massachusetts bank. And what he was looking at was Gamow's tie pin, which read 'alanine', whereas his identifications was as

'Gamow'. So Gamow said to him, 'Oh, I see you're looking at my tie pin and it says alanine. I'll have to explain this to you. Tell me young man, how much do you know about the structure of DNA?' So this RNA Tie Club was a fringe thing you see, and it certainly didn't include trying to change cheques!

When Francis put forward the adaptor hypothesis, which postulated that for each amino acid there'd be an adaptor RNA, and there'd be one enzyme to join the two together, the biochemists said, 'This is utterly impossible, because there will have to be twenty enzymes to do this. And if they existed we biochemists would have already discovered them. And we haven't, so it must be wrong!'"

Nevertheless, biochemists' practical expertise in cell fractionation, purification of cell extracts, and the infant science of cell-free protein synthesis was now required to test the molecular biologist's theories, and protein biochemists had come to work at the Cambridge laboratory.

"As soon as I arrived in Cambridge, Francis and I established the new MRC Molecular Biology Unit. During this period we were doing many things more or less simultaneously. Francis had decided that we should start actively looking for adaptor RNA. So he began this, together with John Littlewood and Mahlon Hoagland who came here in that glorious year [1956], to see whether they could purify transfer RNA and start to work on protein synthesis."

Another problem was the precise nature of the 'RNA template' referred to in Crick's adaptor model. By now, the ribosomes were the accepted site of protein synthesis and, since they were rich in RNA, it was widely assumed that ribosomal RNA was the formal template for amino acid synthesis.

"Now you have to understand that at that time it was believed that the ribosomes carried coding information directly from the gene to the protein. That is, the RNA of the ribosomes was the material that was, so to speak, the informational intermediate. But a lot of experiments seemed to make that very questionable."

Ribosomal RNA accounts for the great majority of RNA in the cell, and so when a cell's total RNA was extracted and analysed using the techniques available at the time, it was essentially the ribosomal RNA that was being analysed. Ribosomal RNAs from different species of bacteria are in fact very similar in sequence.

"One of the experiments that created some concern was a set of analyses of the base composition of RNA and DNA of bacteria. It had been known for some time, and was strongly reinforced during this period, that whereas the base composition – that is, the ratio of the amount of C+G to A+T – varied in [different species of] bacteria over an enormous range, that of the RNA did not. There were bacteria whose DNA was three-quarters G+C, down to bacteria whose DNA was three-quarters A+T. This was accompanied by complete invariance of the RNA. The RNA seemed to have about the same base composition in all the bacteria. This gave rise to a lot of problems because clearly if DNA is carrying the genetic information why did it vary so much? You would have thought that the language of the code was pretty invariant.

There were several kinds of theories to get out of this dilemma. One theory echoed things we think about today. It was that the DNA of bacteria was made up of two kinds. One was invariant and looked like the composition of RNA, while the other kind of DNA was variable: in fact it was just a lot of junk. And again there were 'don't worry' theories as to how to explain this. The 'junk hypothesis' had to be discarded when Paul Doty and his colleagues showed that the dispersion of the base composition of DNA was in fact homogeneous. If the junk theory was correct you would have expected that DNA from different bacteria would split into two distinct fractions – one that corresponded to the bulk analysis and a smaller fraction which would have been the genes."

In addition to the problematical observation that the base composition of DNA varied so much among different bacterial species whereas that of bulk RNA did not, another experimental observation begged an explanation – the robust synthesis of phage head protein after the phage infected bacterial cells.

"Another of the things [we] were trying to work on was the gene–protein problem. As the gene–protein problem went ahead we discovered that a protein that was very easy to purify in very large amounts was the so-called head protein of the bacteriophage. The amazing thing is that when one studied what happened after infection with bacteriophage, this single protein accounted for 70% of all the protein synthesis of the cell.

This prodigious synthesis was something that we knew had to be explained. It was known that after phage infection no new *bacterial* proteins were made. So the phage in a sense captured the bacteria for its own purposes. If you believed that the ribosomal RNA carried the information from gene to protein, you had to assume that the markedly increased rate of *phage* protein synthesis resulted from new ribosomes being made after phage infection. Since the synthesis of just one phage protein – the head protein – accounted for 70% of new protein synthesis, one would have expected at least a 70% increase in new ribosomes. The difficulty was that it was clear that after phage infection *no* new ribosomes were made.

There was no detectable new RNA synthesis! So what you had was what I called at that time the 'paradox of the prodigious rate of protein synthesis'. You had to say that there could be a few new ribosomes made which might have escaped your attention, but if so, clearly these very few were capable of *prodigious* rates of function.

Other people were working on this question of RNA – of information transfer – at the time, and some years before, two workers called Elliot Volkin and Lazarus Astrachan had discovered a very small fraction of RNA that was made after phage infection, which had a base composition resembling that of the phage DNA rather than the bacterial DNA.[4] Volkin and Astrachan actually thought that this was an intermediate in DNA synthesis. But the mystery of Volkin–Astrachan RNA lingered. One of the problems, of course, was that you couldn't be too sure that there was not a small fraction of cells that had escaped the block of phage synthesis that were doing this. But other people began to work on this RNA made after phage infection, and their work suggested that this new RNA was in fact found in the presence of a small number of ribosomes."

Volkin and Astrachan's finding that in phage-infected E. coli *a new and very short-lived RNA species could be detected that had a base ratio precisely complementary to the phage DNA is a famous case of missed opportunity in molecular biology history. This RNA was in fact an, admittedly obscure, clue to the elusive intermediate between the genetic code embodied in DNA and the site of protein synthesis – the ribosomes. However, the importance of the discovery was not appreciated by Volkin*

4.   Volkin E and Astrachan L. **Intracellular distribution of labeled ribonucleic acid after phage infection of** *Escherichia coli.* *Virology* 1956; **2**:433–437.

and Astrachan, or for a while by anyone else. As Judson describes:

"Their first report, completed in March, and the paper that Volkin had read on the matter at the McCollum–Pratt Symposium in Baltimore in June 1956, had been apologetic to an extreme about the possibility of contaminated experiments, uncertain about conclusions. Besides that, they thought that their radioactive RNA, resembling phage DNA in base composition, was converted into DNA for new phage particles. Crick [and Brenner] was not in that audience. He read the results when they were published later that year. The notion of an RNA precursor to DNA did not fit the biochemistry of DNA synthesis that Kornberg had elucidated. The Volkin and Astrachan RNA was an anomaly. It could not quite be dismissed as the inconsequential and self-admittedly sloppy work of people not well known, at a lab not highly regarded." [Judson, p325, p427, see footnote 10, Chapter 2]

Volkin–Astrachan RNA kept its secret for another four years. Insight came suddenly during an informal meeting in Brenner's rooms at King's College, Cambridge on Good Friday of 1960. The laboratories were closed that day because of the holiday, but a group of scientists were visiting after attending a meeting of the Microbiological Society in London.

"At this time, people working in Paris – François Jacob and Jacques Monod – had come to the independent conclusion that no new ribosomes are made during increased protein synthesis in bacteria. They had been studying the regulation of gene expression, and they needed something special to explain the rapid induction of the enzyme β-galactosidase under certain conditions. They had been studying the kinetics of expression of β-galactosidase after you induced the gene for β-galactosidase in a bacterial cell by growing cells in lactose, and found that this happened extremely rapidly. They had done a lot of experiments to try and explain this and had produced a number of alternatives, all of which just seemed quite strange. For example, one of their alternatives was that the gene for this enzyme instructed protein synthesis directly – there was no intermediate. But they seemed to have firmly excluded the possibility that new ribosomes were made to carry out this rapid protein synthesis or, if they were, they were a very small fraction of ribosomes capable of prodigious synthesis.

I met François Jacob in the late 1950s when I went to Paris to give a lecture on bacteriophage, and that is when our friendship really dates from. He came over to Cambridge – this would be April 1960 – and a famous meeting took place in my rooms in King's College, which has been recounted in the autobiographies of both Francis Crick and François Jacob."

Those present at this historic meeting included Brenner, Jacob, Crick, the Dane Ole Maaløe, Alan Garen and his wife Susan from the United States, and Leslie Orgel. In his autobiography, Jacob related that:

"Francis and Sydney wanted to discuss in detail our experiments. They made me take a veritable examination! With questions, criticisms, comments. A pack of hounds racing around me, nipping at my heels. I was, however, in a position of strength. If it hadn't been for their rapid-fire English, I would have felt quite at ease. All the more so as I had new results to report: an experiment long prepared in Paris and recently completed in Berkeley by Arthur Pardee and his student Monica Riley. [This famous experiment was called the PaJaMo *experiment after its architects,* Pardee, Jacob and Monod]. They had succeeded in charging the DNA of male bacteria with radioactive phosphorus; in making them transfer to females the gene of galactosidase; in letting*

them synthesise the enzyme for some minutes and then in destroying the gene through the disintegration of the radioactive phosphorus. The result was clear: once the gene was destroyed, all synthesis stopped. No gene, no enzyme. Which excluded any possibility of a stable intermediary [such as ribosomal RNA]." [Jacob, p311–312][5]

"It was remarkable in the sense that nobody was in possession of all the pieces of information. The people in Paris didn't know about Volkin–Astrachan RNA; they didn't know about phage. We knew about that stuff but we couldn't see the significance until it was actually all laid out on that day. What I remember very clearly is that we were discussing the so-called *'PaJaMo'* [pronounced pajama] experiment. Suddenly it occurred to me that the Volkin–Astrachan RNA must be what I called at that meeting the 'messenger RNA'. There was a moment during the course of this which was absolutely uncanny. You got the feeling that only Francis Crick and I knew what each other were talking about, and that everybody else just couldn't follow what we were saying.

I got very excited and said, 'Volkin–Astrachan; information intermediate; it's short-lived; a short-lived intermediate! It must be! Look at the way it turns over in phage!' And nobody knew what we were talking about because of this sudden jump. But at that moment it became clear to me."

Years later Brenner told Judson that:

"Suddenly I was talking to Francis, and no one else was following me. He picked it

---

5.   Jacob F: *The Statue Within: An Autobiography.* trans. Philip, Franklin. New York: Basic Books, 1988/
      New York: Cold Spring Harbor Press, 1995.

up straight away. I mean, that's the way it suddenly hit me between the eyes, that of all things – there had to be an RNA which was added to the ribosomes." [Judson, p419][6]

Crick's recollection of this critical moment is that:

"Sydney Brenner let out a loud yelp. He had seen the answer. The sudden flash of enlightenment when the idea was first glimpsed was so memorable that I can recall just where Sydney, François and I were sitting in the room when it happened." [Crick, p119, see footnote 3]

"If you talk about two things simultaneously you have a lot of green balls bouncing and you have a lot of red balls bouncing. And sometimes you can just see one set of balls bouncing the same way. I think it is so necessary to continue almost hysterical conversation, just constitutive talking. Because I think that brings things together that you don't actually see by a logical deduction. With most logical deduction you just go around in the same circle, and you need to break out of it. For me the curtain lifted at the moment one saw there was this unstable intermediate. Now one of the unfortunate things, I should say, was that messenger got defined as being unstable. It happens to be unstable in bacteria. But instability was never the essential criterion. Instability was simply required to explain enzyme induction. To explain how fast you could turn induction off. There was no memory for induction so you had to say that you get the message and then you use it up. But this was not the *necessary* concept. The necessary concept was that you add something to a machine which gets instructed by it. It is effectively all

6. Judson HF. *The Eighth Day of Creation* (expanded edition). New York: Cold Spring Harbor Press, 1996.

those old ideas of the von Neumann machine. And to actually be able to say, 'This is the tape!' Of course what you do then is use the analogies that come from everyday life, you know. There were tape recorders just making their appearance then and you said, 'Well, you put the tape in the machine and the machine reads it.' So I think it's that analogical thinking which gives you this.

By the afternoon, François Jacob had come to my house in Cambridge and we had designed the nature of the experiment that had to be done. We realised that we had to show experimentally that this new RNA [messenger RNA] was present on old ribosomes, and we realised immediately that this could be done with bacteriophage."

In his autobiography Crick wrote:

"That evening I held a party at the Golden Helix [his house in Cambridge]. We often had parties, but this one was different. Half the guests were just having a good time. The other half, in small groups, were earnestly discussing the new idea, seeing how it easily explained puzzling data and actively planning radically new key experiments to put the hypothesis to the test." [Crick, p120, see footnote 3]

Brenner realised in a flash that when a gene is expressed, its coded information for a particular protein is handed on to a newly synthesised and short-lived messenger RNA intermediate. This then becomes physically associated with the ribosomes, where it specifies the synthesis and joining of amino acids in a particular sequence. If this view of protein synthesis was correct and universal, then after infection of a bacterial cell by phage, the phage DNA should instruct the synthesis of new *messenger RNA, which should associate exclusively with* pre-existing *bacterial ribosomes, there being, according to the hypothesis, no such thing as 'new' ribosomes.*

To demonstrate this, Brenner and Jacob planned an experiment of great technical dif-ficulty. To distinguish 'old' from 'new', they planned to tag the ribosomes in bacter-ial cells before *infection with phage with isotopes that would make their density heavier than normal. Then, immediately* after *phage infection they would remove the heavy isotopes from the medium so that if any new ribosomes were made they would be of normal density. Normal and heavy ribosomes could be separated by the tech-nique of density gradient centrifugation. If messenger RNA was synthesised imme-diately after phage infection, then this new RNA could also be tagged, this time with radioactive phosphorus added to the medium. If, as they believed, this messenger RNA associated with pre-existing ribosomes and no new ribosomes were made dur-ing phage infection, then* all *the radioactivity should be associated with the heavy ribosomes in the density gradient.*

"And how would we tell the difference between old and new? Well we would do it by the tricks developed by Matthew Meselson and Frank Stahl which they'd used for DNA replication.[7] Namely, we would label these [ribosomes] with heavy isotopes, with carbon-13 and nitrogen-15, and we would be able by density gradi-ent centrifugation just to 'weigh' them and discover whether they were old or new.

But it was one thing to say all of that and another thing to do it. Of course the per-son who had all the amino acids made with the heavy isotopes was in California – that was Matt Meselson. Happily, François was going to California that sum-mer. He had been invited there. And I had been invited to come to California for another reason, and so we fixed it that we would do this experiment in California

7. Meselson M and Stahl FW. **The replication of DNA in** *Escherichia coli. Proc Natl Acad Sci USA* 1958; **44:**671–682.

the following June for a couple of months. I arranged it with Meselson that he'd join us and we'd be able to use his isotopes and his equipment.

I did a preliminary experiment which was never published but in fact is quite interesting because it proved to me that no new ribosomes could be made. This experiment involves the following. If you take bacteria and starve them of magnesium, after a long period of time they lose their ribosomes. They destroy them and turn them over. Now when you start them up again by giving them 'good' medium supplemented with magnesium they take a long time to make new ribosomes, to get going.

So what I said was, 'Well, I'll do a quickie experiment to see if we're on the right ground.' Because if it is true that new ribosomes are made after phage infection, my destroying the old ones shouldn't have any effect and phage production should take off very rapidly. The experiment was beautifully clear. You destroyed the ribosomes and then infected the cells with phage at different periods and asked how much virus could you make? And it went down, and it went down, and there came a point where you didn't see anything in the way of bacteriophage. Because after phage infection you don't make any new ribosomes. I knew then that I had to be right!

So we went to California to do this experiment and that was a hilarious story. We went to do quite a difficult experiment. I mean it's technically complex, and we had to do it in three weeks, and I didn't even know whether it would work – even if we could *get* it to work. One of the terrible things was that everything started to fall apart in the density gradients. The ribosomes were not stable and every experiment failed. These experiments were awful! They took a lot of expensive isotope and you didn't know the answer until you had run it in a centrifuge for a day. And if anything went wrong, if the centrifuge had broken down, it was really terrible. So getting everything through to the end in an intact form was a major thing, and every experiment we did didn't work. I remember people saying, 'Well, you know it's going to take a year of exploratory work, of 'normal science' to do this!'

One of the amusing things was that Max Delbrück didn't believe this hypothesis of the unstable intermediate. But I said to François 'You know we're fine.' And he asked 'Why?' And I replied, 'Because Max doesn't believe in it!' Max was marvellous you know. He was always wrong. George Streisinger tells a story in an essay that he once came out of Max's office looking very depressed and someone asked him 'What's the matter?' George replied, 'Max likes my theory, it must be wrong!' So I told François, 'Don't worry. Max thinks it's wrong, so we must be right!'"

The problem of keeping the ribosomes intact during sedimentation in the ultracentrifuge continued to harass the messenger RNA experiment, and Brenner and Jacob were becoming increasingly despondent.

"Some of the things I tried then were quite interesting. For example, the caesium chloride we were using to centrifuge these ribosomes was eight molar. That's very, very strong salt! I discovered that there are bacteria from the Dead Sea that actually like to live in very strong salt.' So we thought, 'Why don't we try these. You know, they'll have ribosomes that like a lot of salt. I actually got hold of them, but of course we couldn't do the experiment with them because they weren't sensitive to infection by our bacteriophage.'"

In his autobiography Jacob recalled this dispirited phase:

"We had come for the sole purpose of carrying out this experiment that we had no doubt was going to change the world. But the gods were still against us. Nothing worked. Our fine confidence at the start had evaporated. Disheartened, Meselson had departed – to get married! Sydney and I talked about going back to Europe. In a burst of compassion, a biologist by the name of Hildegaard had taken us under her wing and, to give us a change of scene, driven us to a nearby beach. There we were, collapsed on the sand, stranded in the sunlight like beached whales. My head felt empty. Frowning, knitting his heavy eyebrows, with a nasty look, Sydney gazed at the horizon without saying a word.

Never yet had I seen Sydney Brenner in such a state. Never seen him silent. On the contrary, he was an indefatigable talker at every opportunity. A tireless storyteller, able to discourse for days and nights on end. Interminable monologues on every conceivable subject. Science, politics, philosophy, literature, anything that cropped up. With stories he made up as he went along. Generously laced with jokes. With nasty cracks, too, at the expense of just about everyone. An excellent actor, he could render a speech in Hungarian, a lecture in Japanese, mimic Stalin or Franco. He went without a break from one register to another". [Jacob, p310, see footnote 5]

"One day we were lying on a beach. We had gone out to the beach to rest our weary souls. We were starting to feel that we now have to settle down to a long year of really boring analysis and finding the right conditions and so on. And then it just occurred to me that it is magnesium that stabilises the ribosomes and that the caesium must be competing with the magnesium – not very efficiently, but enough to displace it and destabilise the ribosomes. And of course the magnesium we were putting in was only a thousandth molar, while the caesium we had was eight molar. So the thing to do was to raise the magnesium. I sprang up and said 'It's the magnesium, it's the magnesium!' François didn't know what was going on.

But we ran back to the lab and we raised the magnesium. I said, 'Let's put in a lot because we have three tubes and this experiment is the last chance.' So I said, 'Put in a lot. It can do no harm.' He asked, 'One hundredth molar?' I replied, 'All right, but let's have one with one tenth molar also.' So we set up the experiment. François was so nervous he dropped the radioactive phosphate in the water-bath and we hid the water-bath behind the Coca-Cola machine so that they wouldn't find it, because it was now very radioactive. In fact, several years later I came back to Cal Tech and asked, 'Could I have a Coke please?' And they said, 'Oh yes, of course.' I asked, 'Is the machine still in the basement?' I wanted to see if this water bath was still there. It wasn't!

In the middle of the run the centrifuge broke down. You had to spin for a very long time in order to generate a gradient of the salt and then everything sedimented to its proper position. These gradients are tremendously mechanically stable, but they're not thermally stable. And so when the centrifuge broke down we had to move the rotor from one cold room to another cold room. We managed to do this and borrow another centrifuge and start it up again. This day I will never forget! We finally said this is it! Then we had to take the rotor out and take out the caesium from the tubes in drops. I was extremely skilled at this because it was all done by hand. There were no machines and you had to pierce the tube with a needle and then take a rack of tubes and move it by hand, collecting drops as you went. I had to carry the centrifuge from the cold room to this other place and I said, 'I'm not going on the lift [elevator] because the lift will shake it.' So everybody made a path for me so that no one would come barging out of a room.

Now in Cal Tech at that time the cooling in the buildings was done by spraying water into the circulating air. I came out of this cold room with this rotor, walking along as though it was, you know, a great religious thing. And the water condensed on me, so that by the time I got to the lab I was completely wet. My clothes were completely wet, but I couldn't stop. I had to put the rotor down and undo the tubes and François stood there and he was very nervous while I pierced the tubes. The first one I did I had a bit of a shake at the beginning, so I missed the first four drops. But finally we dispensed all three tubes without further incident.

That was actually the day on which the Democratic Party nominated John F Kennedy for the presidential election. And that evening, as we dried all the drops from the gradients, everybody went to the lab to listen to the radio and the television to see Kennedy receiving the nomination. We sat downstairs in the basement with our radioactivity counter, to count the radioactivity in the new RNA and we jokingly said, 'We're going to see if *we* receive a nomination now!' It was very nice because we relaxed there and the counter began to count.

It took a long time to print out. And we got delirious because the radioactivity curve began to rise and I said in French, '*Ascendez, ascendez*. It's rising, it's rising!' Then it went on rising. And then we realised it was time for the radioactivity to drop if the experiment was correct. So we were both shouting at this machine 'Go down, go down, down, down', and the next tube went up a bit. But the increase was less and I said, 'It's less, it's less!' And we were actually striving to bend the numbers. Then the numbers came down and it was absolutely convincing. *That's* the experiment that made it convincing."

A single peak of radioactively labelled RNA coincided precisely with the position of the old ribosomes. There was no evidence of new ribosome synthesis.

"After that we knew we were right and what we had to do then was a lot of subsequent work in order to tidy it up because we had to show that the same ribosomes that we'd programmed with these messengers were the ones that were making protein. I did that in Cambridge when I returned for the rest of 1960, and in the winter of 1960 we wrote our paper and we submitted it to *Nature* just before the end of the year. We then heard that Jim Watson was submitting a paper on the same thing with *his* work on messenger. Our experiments showed that new RNA was added to old ribosomes and his experiments showed that there was an RNA fraction on the ribosomes. So we agreed to wait for him, but he took about another five months and so the paper finally appeared in May of 1961.[8]

The paper is written in a very peculiar style. It proposed three models that might explain how information is transferred. One was that the DNA instructed protein synthesis directly. Another was that there were a small number of new ribosomes made, and the third was that new messenger RNA is made. So the paper discussed the expectations of each of these models and which were eliminated experimentally. We had to do that because the technical side of the paper was very very forbidding. I remember that at a meeting someone got up and said, 'I wish to propose two models A and B. Either model A is correct or model B is correct.' And I said, 'You've forgotten the third alternative, which is that neither is correct!'

8.   Brenner S, Jacob F, Meselson M. **An unstable intermediate carrying information from genes to ribosomes for protein synthesis.** *Nature* 1961; **190:**576–581.

So that is how the messenger came about, and what is remarkable about it is that in a sense it's an experiment that had to be done at that level because no one would ever do anything like that again.

We were still working on mutagenesis at that time, going from one thing to the other. Because what we were interested in was the connection between what's written in the DNA and what's written in the protein. That's really what we wanted to know and we used anything and everything to get at that."

Not everyone was entirely convinced by the messenger experiment.

"I went up to Stanford to give a lecture and I received a long fatherly talk from Arthur Kornberg – which irritated me I have to say – telling me I didn't understand intermediary metabolism. I can remember being quite annoyed and giving him the explanation for four-year-olds of the difference between the apparent and the true base composition, which doesn't depend on pool sizes. You see, most biochemists said, 'Well, this result could be affected by the pool size and by the labelling of it with the tracer.' You could show that wasn't the case. But it took a lot of time to jar people out of this and also to jar them out of the idea that you could actually do an experiment like this and take it as evidence.

You see, it was very popular to have an experiment done in a certain style and then every paper had to be written in that style and you weren't, so to speak, allowed to publish a paper until you'd fulfilled this. So there was a time that, unless you had a sucrose gradient of something, you couldn't publish a paper. There was another time that you had to show a DNA heteroduplex in an electron microscope. I thought one day that I would make one of these things out of a rope on a beach and just photograph it and say, 'I've done the heteroduplex. There it is!'

There was an unfortunate thing at the Cold Spring Harbor Symposium that year. I said, 'We call this messenger RNA.' Because Mercury was the messenger of the gods, you know. And Erwin Chargaff very quickly stood up in the audience and said he wished to point out that Mercury may have been the messenger of the gods, but he was also the god of thieves. Which said a lot for Chargaff at the time! But I don't think that we stole anything from anybody – except from nature. I think it's right to steal from nature, however.

François Jacob was of course extremely pleased with all of this because this wasn't the sort of thing that the people in Paris were doing. And yet it was wonderful to have brought this from another direction and to really be able to reinforce the ideas they had that gene regulation was involved. Because that was what François and Jacques were really interested in – how gene expression was turned on. A little bit later François and I actually did an experiment to prove this, which we published in *Comptes Rendus* and it's gone largely unnoticed. But the first formal proof that induction of gene expression involved new messenger RNA synthesis is in that paper we did together in about 1962. It involved proving that galactokinase messenger is produced only when you induce the galactokinase operon. And it all fitted with the genetics of the operator-constitutive and the operator-zero mutants, which basically said that there was a part of the gene that was a switch, and that you could break this switch in two positions: either ON or OFF. If it was broken OFF you couldn't get anything from it, and if it was broken ON you got it all the time.

François was a geneticist, not a biochemist. He came from phage λ, where all these concepts about repression were first developed. The tradition in Paris was λ. In the rest of the world it was bacteriophage T4. And that was because people in America were totally influenced by Delbrück, who didn't believe in lysogeny. And so nobody had worked on λ until quite recently. On the other hand, Elie Wollman's parents,[9] who had done all the really classic work on lysogeny in the twenties, were a great tradition at the Pasteur Institute. They died in concentration camps during the war and Elie had come to Paris to continue the Wollman tradition, and it was Elie who initiated all that work and in a sense François joined. There were all these papers by Wollman and Jacob with their analysis of induction, which they did with André Lwoff.

And their investigation of lysogeny led to the concept of the phage repressor. And then realising that the β-galactosidase system was similar – isomorphous in fact – led to these two intellectual streams coming together. But certainly the concepts were from phage λ and could not have been developed out of the phages we were using. I knew about lysogeny and I wanted to work on lysogeny with Sir Cyril Hinshelwood. But he wouldn't let me. I think that's quite interesting!

Well, 1961 was a very exciting year. During that year we published two papers. One was on the messenger RNA experiments and the other was on the general nature of the genetic code.[10] Of course that was incredibly exciting. There was still a lot more work to do in order to follow these things up.

But already – I think in 1962 – my interests were turning to different matters. During that year Francis and I began a long series of conversations, which we continued over several years, about what we should do next. It happens in all

---

9. Elisabeth and Eugène Wollman.
10. Crick FHC, Barnett L, Brenner S, Watts-Tobin RJ. **The general nature of the genetic code for proteins.** *Nature* 1961; **192:**1227–1232.

science that when one gets to this stage there seems to be only what the military people call 'mopping up' operations. And of course such was the thrill of doing molecular biology that one didn't want to be involved in that, and one would rather go forward to fresh pastures."

5
Deciphering the genetic code

The discovery of messenger RNA was critical to clarifying the nature of the information transfer from DNA to protein. But the precise nature of the genetic code remained to be explained. What number of bases in a DNA strand specified an amino acid? Which combination of A, T, C and G specified which amino acid? Was the code truly non-overlapping and, if so, how were the sixty-four possible triplet codons for only twenty amino acids accommodated? There were, as yet, no definitive answers to these questions.

Brenner recalls that somewhere around 1957 or 1958 he invented the word 'codon' to describe the nucleotide unit that would specify an amino acid.

"We used that term because we didn't know at the time that the coding units were triplets even though we thought they might be. In those days everybody defined a unit – in the same way physicists defined units. The first person to do that was Seymour Benzer. Benzer defined three units: the 'cistron', which was the unit of complementation; the 'muton', which was the unit of mutation; and the 'recon', which was the unit of recombination. Only one of those has survived – the 'cistron'. The reason the other two didn't survive was that one should always see what one's units sound like in a different language. And since we had numerous French colleagues, the other two didn't survive because one sounded like a sheep, and the other one sounded like the things Paris taxi drivers called each other! In due course we also had the 'operon', which Jacob and Monod used for the unit of genetic expression in bacteria. And that survived. In fact one often thought of giving lectures entitled 'A Night at the Operon'. And the word that François and I invented for the unit of replication was the 'replicon', and the replicon has survived as well."

Meanwhile, Brenner and Crick attacked the solution of the genetic code on multiple fronts, most of them theoretical. While there was a general consensus that amino acids were encoded by triplets – three consecutive nucleotides – in DNA, there was absolutely no proof that this was indeed the case. Other possibilities, notably a quadruplet code, had to be considered. Experimental evidence for the triplet code was ultimately provided by Crick and Brenner in 1961, through a set of brilliant genetic experiments that had their beginnings in chemical mutagenesis studies initiated by Brenner and Benzer, and their dream that the genetic code might be broken by pure phage genetics (see Chapter 3).

Before his year in Cambridge in 1957–58, Seymour Benzer and Ernest Freese (a colleague at Purdue) had mapped mutations in the rII gene of phage T4 made using 5-bromouracil, an analogue of thymine with different base-pairing properties. These studies defined a collection of sites in the rII *gene that were targets for mutation by*

5-bromouracil – its mutational spectrum. This experimental approach was extended

to include other base analogues, and other mutagenic chemicals, such as nitrous acid,

with known chemical actions on the bases. Brenner also used a drop in pH to

achieve mutation.

"I made mutants by just treating phage at pH 4.5. We knew that at this pH bases are removed – they get depurinated and then you get mutations. I then measured the pH of Coca-Cola and I discovered that it is considerably lower than 4.5. So I thought of writing a paper on acid mutagenesis, saying that I had done this by putting bacteriophage in Coca-Cola, and sending it to the Coca-Cola company saying, 'I'm at a loss to know where to publish this. Have you any useful suggestions?'

Seymour had been doing work on the induction of mutants by chemicals before he came [to Cambridge] and had shown that if you incorporated 5-bromouracil into the phage you got mutants. If you treated it with various other agents you also got mutants. And what had been developed was this idea of mutational spectra. He and I started some work on this – in a desultory way. We had all of these spectra and the question was what did these spectra mean? A remarkable thing that we noticed was that the induced mutants were at different places from the spontaneous mutants, and that the induced mutants could be made to revert by the same class of reagents that induced them, but none of the spontaneous mutants could be made to revert by the so-called base analogue mutagens, and this was a puzzle.

Well, at that time I thought that we should do something completely different so I said to Seymour, 'You know there's a compound called proflavine [a yellow acridine dye], which I've been interested in for some time. It combines with DNA and it also interferes with phage assembly. There's a paper by Bob Demars in which he says he's made mutants with proflavine. So why don't we do an *rII* spectrum with this?' So Lesley Barnett, a technician in the lab, started to do this – started to make mutants with proflavine and started to map them. And what do you know? We found that none of the proflavine mutants could be induced to revert by base analogues and none of the base analogue mutants could be made to revert by proflavine."

These perplexing observations hinted at the possibility that proflavine and the base analogues all caused mutations by different mechanisms. After moving from Purdue to join Watson's laboratory at Harvard, Freese had organised the results of his studies on base analogues and other chemical mutagens into a paper,[1] in which he coined the now standard terms 'transition' mutations and 'transversion' mutations. Transitions are when a purine is replaced by another purine (ie, A replaced by G) or a pyrimidine by another pyrimidine (ie, C replaced by T); transversions are when a purine is replaced by a pyrimidine or vice versa.

But whereas Freese had provided a plausible explanation for mutagenesis by the simple base analogues, there was no clue about how proflavine mutagenesis worked. Brenner told Judson that "For two years that sat and gnawed at us."

"I had a long interest in these damn acridine dyes, and talking in the Eagle pub one time Crick and I went through some tortuous reasoning that clarified the moment one said it. I said, 'What would happen if there were not only transitions

---

1. Freese E. **On the molecular explanation of spontaneous and induced mutations.** *Brookhaven Symp* 1959; **12**:63–75.

and transversions caused by simple base substitution, but also base additions and deletions?' And I suddenly realised that you could get that if you stuck proflavine into the DNA – if it went between the base pairs. This was something that was thought to happen – it was called intercalation. You might then have a situation where the DNA thought that the dye molecule was another base and the cell stuck in an extra base on the other strand during DNA replication, or made a compensating deletion during replication. So the whole idea emerged of some connection between mutations and base additions and deletions. This then said, we realised that acridines would have a drastic effect on this process because they could stick between the bases all over the place."

This realisation that mutations could be caused by base substitution or base deletion eventually provided the route to an experimental proof of the triplet nature of the genetic code. Crick had independently become interested in the molecular basis of the phenomenon of suppression of mutations. The term 'suppression' had been coined to describe the reversion of a mutant to its original phenotype by means of a second mutation, whether occurring spontaneously or after chemical treatment. At the time, the favoured explanation for suppression was that if a mutation resulted in a change in a particular amino acid that altered the structure, and hence the function of a protein, then a second mutation that altered a different amino acid in the protein could compensate for the initial structural change, thereby restoring the function of the protein. But Crick evolved a different hypothesis about suppression:

"Pondering on how an RNA molecule could act as a message, I wondered if it could fold back on itself, thus forming a loose double-helical structure. The idea was that some bases could pair [with the DNA] whereas others, which did not match according to the [base] pairing rules, would loop out. The 'code' would then depend either

on the looped-out bases or the paired ones, or some elaborate combination of these two possibilities. The idea was really rather vague, but it made one important prediction. A mutant at one end of the message might, in theory, be capable of being compensated in its effect by another, toward the other end, that paired with it. Thus, some mutants should have distant 'suppressors' as they are called, within the same gene."
[Crick, p125, see footnote 3, Chapter 4]

"Francis started to play around in the lab with mutants. He started with a few of the base analogue mutants and these didn't give him much joy. But where he found innumerable suppressors was with the acridine mutants. So you could start with a mutant and you could get lots of changes that compensated for it. And it became very difficult to explain this very complex set of relationships by something that interacted at the protein level, although you couldn't exclude it. We all knew that it was possible to get a mutation in one place which would alter a protein, and then you could get another mutation elsewhere which corrected the protein. It's called an internal suppressor. But it was very difficult to explain the extent to which Francis was observing this."

The notion of mutations caused by base additions and deletions tied in with earlier thinking about what was then called the comma-less code, one of the many abstract attempts to understand the nature of the genetic code, and which in fact turned out to be incorrect.

"A brilliant theory had been produced by John Griffith, Leslie Orgel and Francis, called the comma-less code. What they did is ask whether you can find a sequence of consecutive triplets which can only be read in one frame, so that every other frame is nonsense. In fact, you can do this and you can prove that it gives you exactly twenty sense codons. Again the magic number, the number of amino acids, comes out. So you can indeed write codes called comma-less codes where in one frame it makes sense and in every other frame it makes nonsense. That gives you twenty sense triplets and forty-four nonsense triplets. [There are in fact not forty-four nonsense codons. But the redundancy of the genetic code by which multiple different codons can specify a single amino acid was not yet recognised.] What we wanted to know in order to explain acridine-induced mutagenesis suppression was how frequently is there nonsense in the code. Because clearly, if a lot of triplets correspond to nonsense you should have very frequent targets for destroying the meaning of a message.

So this model suggested that if you changed the phase of the triplet read-out by adding bases or deleting them, you would make a mess of the rest of the code. And putting all these things together, the whole basis of internal suppression began to make 'sense' to us. We wrote a paper called 'The theory of mutagenesis',[2] in which we proposed that in addition to the base substitution mutants caused by the traditional chemical mutagens, there were addition and deletion mutations. And this all made sense with experiments showing that some mutations were revertible by base analogues and some were not.

So the acridine experiments went on and they made some very interesting predictions. To give you an example, you could start with a mutant which was arbitrarily called 'plus' because it had gained a base. Then all the suppressors of it would be 'minuses', because when you add a plus and a minus you come back to zero."

---

2.   Brenner S, Barnett L, Crick FHC *et al*. **The theory of mutagenesis.** *J Mol Biol* 1961; 3:121–124.

As an example, if we add the base X to the hypothetical triplet codon sequence CAT CAT CAT CAT, we will shift the reading frame to yield XCA TCA TCA TCA T– –. These triplets may no longer specify the correct amino acids for that position in the protein, or they may not specify any amino acids at all, and so a mutation is observed. Now suppose the effect of this mutation can be compensated for (suppressed) if we introduce a second change in the DNA which deletes the first C, yielding XAT CAT CAT CAT. Even though the first triplet codon CAT is now changed to XAT, this could easily be inconsequential because if there is redundancy in the code, then the codons CAT and XAT could code for the same amino acid. Even if they are not redundant, the single amino acid change might be inconsequential to the function of the protein. The key point is that the subsequent codons CAT are now back in normal register.

"This concept of a phase shift, or a 'frameshift' as we later called it, was so foreign to people in genetics that we had endless problems trying to explain this work."

It did not take Brenner and Crick long to realise that by shifting the phase of the code, essentially at will, by using intercalating agents such as proflavine, they should be able to determine the size of a codon. If a gene was mutated because the codon reading frame had been shifted by one *added base (a so-called plus one frameshift), then the* total *number of base additions (or deletions) to get back into normal frame, into a sense register, should equal the number of nucleotides in a codon.*

"All we had to ask is how many of these mutations could we put together and so come back to the normal phase. So the question was how do you do this experiment uniquely? And the experiment had to be done uniquely in the following way. Let's say that we make three independent single-base addition (or deletion) mutations in the same gene involving bases A, B, C all in a row, and by brute force we make the double mutant AB, and the double mutant BC. If we cross these phages there should be no way a normal phage can be produced because *all* the recombinants will share the mutation B. So if you actually observe wild-type functional phage, this has to be the triple mutant ABC. So we showed that we could actually construct functional triple mutants and therefore the phase of the code was three.

This I think is the kind of apotheosis of a genetic analysis, because you have to consider what you're doing here: you're taking these viruses and you are just mixing them together and you are simply recording plus and minus. And from this pattern it seems mad that you could deduce the actual triplet nature of the genetic code. But this is simply the logic of how the genetic information is trans-ferred – it's a non-overlapping triplet code. This was very hard for geneticists to stomach. That you could take a set of mutants and pair them in many ways and they were still mutant. But if you put three mutants together they came back to normal! And if you mixed four or five they were still mutant. We went as far as six to make it normal and after that it got a bit boring. But formally we showed that the code is a multiple of three. It's $3n$ bases, where n is likely to be 1. That was deduced completely from this experiment.

Now I have to tell you that there were exceptions. There were some things that didn't obey the rules. And a question one can ask is whether in science one should at least tell people about this. What we had was a huge body of information which was entirely self-consistent, but with a concept of the barriers. That is, certain frameshifts generated mutants themselves and therefore were not compatible. And the question is what happens to all these exceptions? Well, you have the 'don't worry hypothesis' – there'll be an explanation for them.

As it turned out it took about five more years to work through all the exceptions, and the remarkable thing is that each one of them had a different and special explanation. For example, there was one double mutant which appeared to suppress itself. We could never isolate its suppressor. And it turned out that this mutation had duplicated itself, and thereby introduced the third phase shift. So this was a completely different explanation. In another instance, even though we made a strong prediction that no base analogue mutants should be revertible by acriflavine and *vice versa*, we found some. It turned out that those were due to new start signals being produced.

So when one encounters something like this, it tells one that if one gets exceptions which cannot explain the coherent theory, the theory should remain. And it was wise of us to take all of these exceptions, which showed no relationship amongst each other, and put them on one side. We didn't conceal them, we put them in an Appendix.

The other interesting thing about this was that it was a real 'house of cards' theory. You had to buy everything. You couldn't take one fact and let it stand by itself and say the rest could go. Everything was so interlocked. You had to buy the plus and minuses, you had to buy the barriers, you had to buy the triplet phase, and all these went together. It was the whole that explained it, and if you attacked any one part of it the whole thing fell apart. So it was an all or nothing theory. And it was very hard to communicate to people.

However, this was one of the most beautiful, aesthetically elegant experiences of my life, in which just by doing these little operations you landed up with this detailed description of the molecular structure of living matter. And all of these things were happening at the same time in 1960 to 1961, at the time when we were still in the old Cavendish laboratories.

I had a lab in the old Anatomy Department at that time. Francis had become extremely skilled at extracting space from various departments. Our phage lab was in an old museum in zoology, which had a whale in it at one time. We borrowed the space from the Professor of Zoology. It was a wonderful lab because it was like a corridor with a row of windows, and what was so interesting is that we had a lot of visitors in the lab and we used to watch the people walking by. And you could say to someone, 'Oh you see that man, that's Professor Dirac.' There was a restaurant at the Friar House with a tea room, and once we looked in and there was a man sitting with an elderly lady. And I said to my friend, 'Just have a look in that tea room. There are two people who changed the world.' It was Otto Frisch and his aunt Lise Meitner sitting there!"

Brenner and Crick published their observations in the last issue of Nature *for 1961, in a landmark paper entitled 'The general nature of the genetic code for proteins' [see Chaper 4, footnote 10]. Now that it was established that the genetic code was a non-overlapping triplet code, the major remaining question was: which triplet of bases specified which amino acid? Here the genius of elegant genetic experiments deserted Brenner and Crick, and they resorted to biochemical approaches. But there were now other, better equipped biochemical teams in the race.*

"It became obvious to both ourselves and to many other people that we could now add messengers to ribosomes and we should get them to produce something

– but [we were] so naïve. We started experiments in Cambridge – I had a post-doc who came to try this – and our idea was to add viral RNAs to *E. coli* ribosomes because we thought that we should be able to play any tape. We knew that these viral RNAs have information because they are the genetic information. We could get them in high amounts and so we started with turnip yellow mosaic virus, trying to add it to *E. coli* ribosomes in an *in vitro* protein synthetic system to see if we could get some protein made, and then we'd show that it's viral protein.

Now when I gave my [messenger RNA] paper at Cold Spring Harbor in the summer of 1961, the people from Severo Ochoa's[3] lab heard this and they too realised that you should be able to add things to ribosomes and make proteins. And so they also began adding RNAs, and so did Marshall Nirenberg.[4] He started with tobacco mosaic virus [TMV], trying to add it to *E. coli* ribosomes. Of course we know now that you won't get anything, because these are eukaryotic messengers and they require a whole set of factors which are not present in bacteria.

The story of adding synthetic polymers, which Ochoa and also Nirenberg did, was the first breakthrough in decoding. The Ochoa group claimed that they realised that this might work and decided to have a go. They didn't know much about translation initiation factors, which was good for them. That's where ignorance triumphed! And Nirenberg, the story goes, was working with TMV and it was suggested that he use a synthetic polymer as a control to get nothing. Because

---

3. At the New York University School of Medicine. In 1959, Severo Ochoa was awarded the Nobel Prize for Physiology or Medicine (jointly with Arthur Kornberg) for his work on elucidating the biological mechanisms of nucleic acid synthesis.
4. Marshall Nirenberg, working at the National Institutes of Health, Robert Holley and Har Gobind Khorana were awarded the Nobel Prize for Physiology or Medicine in 1968 for their work on the interpretation of the genetic code and its function in protein synthesis.

a synthetic polymer of Us would be meaningless. And of course he found a lot of incorporation of phenylalanine. And so a lot of people then began to do this. Gobind Khorana[4] did a lot of work using repeating polymers. So all that work finally led to the definition of the genetic code by direct analysis through RNAs and ribosomes. But these experiments were conceptually implausible until the concept of the messenger.

One of the things that I think was bad in Britain at that time was our very poor abilities in this kind of biochemistry. All the biochemistry was still very old-fashioned. Whereas in America the people emerging from the laboratories of Ochoa and Kornberg[5] had by this time a huge armoury of materials. In fact, in the Kornberg laboratories at Stanford, when a student came in his first job was to make materials for the research, like prepare an enzyme. So getting into the technology with that kind of strategic approach and getting that tradition, working on coding synthesis and DNA replication – well there was hardly any of that in Europe. And we realised that we would have to do some of this. In fact we resolved thereafter that we would develop this type of biochemistry. Francis was always keen to do this. We didn't have the resources in the Cavendish. But when we moved to the new building we built up a lot of this biochemical capability.

But you know, doing things by biochemistry just seemed awfully brute force. We had come to the position of prizing ingenuity beyond anything else, and elegance in the sense of being able just to toss out an experiment and say something profound from it. Although I do think that was more a put on than reality, because the lack of that kind of impetus, that kind of school of biochemistry, really did

5.   Arthur Kornberg. Nobel Prize for Chemistry in 1989 for the discovery of the catalytic properties of RNA.

hold things back in Britain."

Nevertheless, Brenner and his collaborators continued to exploit microbial genetics in ingenious and profitable ways. One of their triumphs was to decipher the triplet codons that encoded the STOP signals during normal protein synthesis, thereby terminating the polypeptide chain.

"There was a single experiment, which was really the kind of last dying whimper – a little bang I would say – of the original programme. The original programme was to examine the sequence of a protein and then, by doing genetics on the DNA with chemical mutagenesis, to work out the sequence of the DNA. And the only place where that succeeded was with the nonsense codons. And that went roughly as follows.

It was known that some mutations gave you nonsense. This had been discovered in the *rII* gene by Benzer, who had invented a little trick in which he constructed an *rII* gene fusion and showed that he could turn off the function of gene B by some mutations in the upstream gene A. These mutants were 'drastic mutants'. We later used this system to show that proflavine had very drastic effects. So we had this idea that they were nonsense mutants but we didn't know what they were. So we started to work on them and found that they were suppressible. We had strains of *E. coli* on which these nonsense mutants grew, and strains on which they didn't. In fact, Seymour used these strains to get nonsense mutants in other genes. They asked themselves at Cal Tech, 'Can we get similar mutants for other genes?' They called all the graduate students together and said, 'We want you to pick and stab phage plaques from agar plates because you have to test many plaques individually. The first person who finds such a mutant we will call this after his mother.' Well, the first student to find such a mutant was a man called Hilliard Bernstein. Now you couldn't call them 'Bernstein mutants'! But Bernstein is the German for 'amber'. So these mutants were called amber mutants. And then we discovered another nonsense mutant, and because the amber had been called amber, I called them 'ochre' mutants. There was a third kind of nonsense that we suspected, but which took us a long time to find. Eventually we did find it, but by that time we'd got tired of these colours. They had already been called 'opal' by someone else, and that they remained. I thought for a moment that I would call them 'umber' mutants, but then I realised this wouldn't go down in England, because there are parts of England where 'amber' is 'umber' and 'umber' is 'oomber'. So there'd be a lot of confusion!

I wondered what happens when you get a nonsense mutation – when you don't have an amino acid. Do you just stop protein synthesis? Or does the ribosome get stuck? So I had the idea that there were two kinds of nonsense. One got stuck, and one actually chain-terminated. And so I said, 'Maybe there's a nonsense mechanism for actually terminating the polypeptide chain during normal protein synthesis.' And if this is the case, then when you get a nonsense mutation the same thing happens, but you can suppress it by carrying on the chain. These would be nonsense suppressors.

The chain-terminating thing did not find much favour in the lab because it was very hard to prove. However, we decided to have a go at it. We knew that the bacteriophage head protein, our old friend, constitutes 70% of the phage protein synthesis. So we decided we'd have a look to see if fragments of this protein were made in nonsense mutants.

Any time a nonsense (STOP) codon was generated by mutation, the protein chain would terminate. The presence of random nonsense mutants would therefore yield multiple random protein fragments of different sizes.

The first experiment was done by a graduate student of mine called Anand Sarabhai, from whose success came the slogan in the lab 'the luck of the Sarabhais'. Anand was a fearless experimenter. He believed in having a go at anything. So even though he was judiciously advised by Francis not to do this experiment because it was bound not to work, he decided to have a go. And of course it worked!

And then we realised that we didn't really have to go through the experiment the way that Anand did. We could use a little trick that Fred Sanger had been using which involved radioactive labelling of the protein and fingerprinting. And of course we now suddenly realised that since we had all these *amber* mutants in this gene we could give a topological proof of co-linearity. And we wouldn't have to do any protein sequencing! The only assumption we would have to make is that the protein is always read from the same end, which seemed a very reasonable one. So in 1964 we published a paper which proved that the gene and the protein were co-linear by an argument that was totally unexpected at that time. We showed that as the amber mutations moved further and further to the right in the position of the gene, we got progressively more and more of the protein made.

Now what still remained very interesting to me was whether we could work out the codon triplets for these nonsense mutants. The experiment was a very straightforward one, and in fact is still being used by people to teach present-day students the principles of analytical molecular genetics. Because it's a very exceptional example of what you can say from the DNA almost by genetics alone. Of course, one knew from the genetic code that ambers and ochres and UGAs were connected. By making certain assumptions about mutations induced by hydroxyl-amine, I could decide whether I was going from C to U, or G to A at sites of mutation. But I'd have to know which of the two DNA strands was affected and then I'd have to decode the mutant triplet codon. So the experiment went like this.

It asked, 'How many mutants do you record immediately after chemical mutagenesis on a restrictive [normal] strain and how many do you get on an unrestricted [suppressor] strain?' The mutants that are missing in the first set must be those that are affected in the sense DNA strand. That was a lot of work, but it was easy. It simply involved making a lot of mutants and mapping them. You had to generate two mutant spectra and then find out what was missing in one. You could then work out whether you had a C or a G in the coding strand. And because we had shown what amino acids in the head protein gave rise to the amber triplets, we could say that if these amino acids are such and such, then the amber and the ochre triplets must be this and this. Of course we could not tell the order of the bases, but we could tell that they had to be either UAG, which was the amber, or UAA, which was the ochre, or AUG. I was able to work out that all the nonsense codons had a U. One of them had a U and two As, one of them had a U and an A and a G, and the third also had a U and an A and a G, but the sequence was the other way around. And so putting this all together I worked out that the most likely sequence for the three nonsense codons was UAA, UAG, and UGA. So, by just that experiment – hydroxylamine mutagenesis – and a lot of information about what amino acid codons were, we fulfilled just the last bit of the original programme of sequencing DNA. So I'd like to say that I did sequence three bases in DNA by genetics alone. Had we gone on plodding in this way we might have been able to work out the whole of the code. But that was the last of this sort of thing. From then on it all became biochemistry.

In 1962, we moved to the new lab, where in fact we continued work on nonsense suppression. The simplest idea of [nonsense] suppression was that it involved mutations in the transfer RNA [tRNA] genes of the *E. coli* host. So, for example, instead of a tRNA reading the normal codon UAC, it could now read UAG, a nonsense codon. We knew that one way of proving this was to work out the sequence of tRNA in these beasts. But in this field, the whole drama of doing it by genetics alone had disappeared, and so this was when one began to turn one's mind to other things.

But in the interim we had a very large number of very high level, dedicated post-doctoral fellows, largely from America, who came during this period to work on molecular genetics with us. And of course the suppressors and the tRNAs were available for lots of projects and many people cut their teeth on this and made themselves famous as a result, including Howard Goodman, John Abelson, Malcolm Gefter and Sidney Altman. In fact through this work Sidney Altman went on to discover RNA processing and was later awarded the Nobel Prize with Tom Cech."

In those early days, the laboratory teemed with ideas, people and projects, and work was made more pleasurable by the absence of any significant competition.

"It was a very comforting thing that no one else in the world was working on a project. That's the greatest thing for morale in a lab. Because if you sit in a laboratory and you think, 'My God, there are a hundred labs working on this project and each of these have forty people in them. That's four thousand to one that I'm not going to win.' These are terrible odds and that simply means that no one does anything. What is wonderful is to be able to say, 'This is exclusive, so to speak, at this stage and we can do this without having the hordes come in and industrialise it.' I always believed that the best thing in science is to work out of phase. That is, either half a wavelength ahead or half a wavelength behind. It doesn't matter. As long as you're out of phase with the fashion you can do new things!"

Brenner's parents

Oxford, 1953, at the time of Crick and Watson's double helix announcement

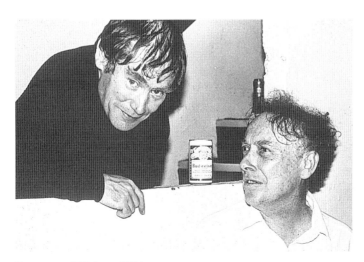

Brenner and Watson, 1974

With Gunther Stent and Josh and Esther Lederberg, 1965

With Max Perutz, 1979

6
DNA replication
dissected

In the 1953 Nature *paper in which Watson and Crick announced the structure of DNA, they included the famous sentence in which they hint at a model for replication of the genetic material. "It has not escaped our notice that the specific pairing [of bases] we have postulated immediately suggests a possible copying mechanism for the genetic material." [see Chapter 2, footnote 5]*

A direct confirmation of this mode of DNA replication, by which each parent strand of DNA acted as a template for new strand synthesis, was provided in a classic experiment carried out in the late 1950s by Matthew Meselson and Franklin Stahl [see Chapter 4, footnote 7], who pioneered the use of the isotopic labelling techniques so elegantly exploited later by Brenner and Jacob (with Meselson's help) in the discovery of messenger RNA. The biochemistry of DNA replication was attacked by several investigators, most prominently Arthur Kornberg[1] and his colleagues at Stanford University, who first demonstrated DNA synthesis in a cell-free system and discovered the enzyme they called DNA polymerase – the enzyme that catalyses the process of DNA synthesis by copying information from each of the parent strands, as predicated by Watson and Crick. Another aspect of DNA replication had caught Brenner's interest, that of exactly how a DNA molecule was replicated in vivo *so that a copy was passed on to each daughter cell.*

"At that time, DNA replication was in the hands of the biochemists and they thought it was very straightforward. You just have an enzyme called DNA polymerase, which Arthur Kornberg had worked on and discovered, and you had DNA and you gave it some substrates, and so you had the equation: DNA plus DNA polymerase plus four triphosphates gives you more DNA. That was the end of the story as far as the biochemists were concerned. But Jacob and I were not interested in just copying DNA. We wanted to know how this DNA would be segregated – given to daughter cells. Would you have to copy the DNA from many sites, which is what the biochemists had at least a picture of, or from some single unique site? And how would you regulate this? Because a bacterial cell copies DNA exactly once, takes the daughters, and segregates them to different cells. Our idea was that DNA replication started at one place, so we had an element which we initially called the 'replicon', but which later became the 'origin of replication'. Namely, something had to appear which said 'Start here and go on doing it'.

---

1. Arthur Kornberg was awarded the Nobel Prize for Physiology or Medicine in 1959 (jointly with Severo Ochoa) for his work on the biological mechanisms of nucleic acid synthesis.

So the concept was that it wouldn't matter what DNA was attached to that unit. It would just be copied. Later that became the whole basis of genetic engineering. Because if a bacterial DNA could, so to speak, only identify its own DNA as opposed to anything else you put into it, that would have made all of this genetic engineering impossible. But we took the view that DNA is DNA; it's just bases, and if you attach it to the right replication unit then it will be copied willy-nilly. So we proposed to test our hypothesis by a series of experiments.

Bacteria have elements called *F* elements, which can be transferred from one bacterium to another by a process of conjugation. That was work that had been done by Bill Hayes, and of course extensively by Jacob and Wollman in their study of bacterial conjugation – sex between bacteria. They proved that the chromosome, when it was attached to an *F* element, was progressively transferred from one point in one given direction. It would take about two hours to transfer the whole chromosome from one cell to another.

We thought that a good driving force for this was the replicon. So our idea was that, in a bacterial cell carrying an *F* element, the *F* element was rather special in that it started from a point of origin and then by replication it would drive the chromosome across the cell. And if it did this it would transfer a daughter chromosome. We knew that the dye acridine orange cured *F* factors. That is, if you grew cells carrying *F* factors in acridine orange they lost them. We argued that for some reason or another the replication of this *F* factor was sensitive to this dye. Therefore, if transfer was simply due to the mechanics of replication we should be able to stop chromosome transfer with acridine orange. However, there was no sign that acridine orange actually inhibited DNA replication. So our argument was that once replication got started you couldn't stop transfer with acridine orange. You could only stop its *initiation*.

François and I discussed all this in the spring of 1962 at a meeting in Royaumont. We went home and we both did the experiment the next day and we phoned each other that we'd got the same result."

> *The demonstration in these experiments that acridine orange stopped the* initiation *of DNA replication but not its* continuation, *supported the notion of a special replicon, or unique site of replication initiation, in the chromosome.*

"We proceeded to do more experiments. In fact we planned a rather complicated experiment. But we decided that since the theory was so good we would write it up in advance. So we went on a combined family holiday to a French seaside resort called La Tranche, which we used to refer to as *Zee Slice,* in the Vendée. We spent hours on the beach telling children not to pester us while we developed the whole idea of the replicon and how to test it experimentally.

One of the important experiments was very tricky to do. We wanted to show that the DNA transferred from the male into the female bacterium had been replicated once before transfer. We proposed to do this by Meselson–Stahl experiments. (Meselson and Stahl had labelled DNA with heavy atoms, nitrogen and carbon. And they had then shown that DNA replicated semiconservatively, that is, each parental strand acquired a new daughter.)

This was extremely difficult to do. However, the experiment was done and in fact did show that the DNA that came across from the male to the female was indeed a hybrid DNA that had been replicated once. However, we could not say for certain that the DNA had been copied in the donor cell. The equivalent explanation is that rather than having replication driving the DNA across in the male, you could equally have an enzyme in the female which pulled it across by exactly the same method. And we could not resolve these questions.

These experiments with François continued throughout 1962, and in that year we also got the idea that we should study DNA replication in some depth. The way to do this we thought was to isolate temperature-sensitive mutants for DNA replication. So in that year I started a rather large project together with François to look for temperature-sensitive mutants of *E. coli*, which we did. We developed many many ways of doing this quickly. And among these we found quite a number that were defective in DNA replication. If, as we had predicted, there was a replicon required to start DNA replication, then a mutant of that, we argued, would not allow a bacterium to start DNA replication, and therefore these bacteria should be blocked at the start in this cycle of replication.

That work developed on quite a large scale, and many of the mutants we isolated later became famous. There wasn't just one gene making one enzyme that was required for DNA replication. The mutations got as far as 'Z' in the alphabet, which meant that there were at least twenty-six of these genes. And some of the early ones, like *dnaA*, which is the name of one of the elements involved in initiating DNA replication, was the first one characterised, and then we had *dnaB*, which helps as well to do this, and *dnaC* and *D*, and so on.

We started to characterise these mutants with collaborators at the Pasteur Institute, and to show that some of them were involved in initiation. So that once the chromosome initiated replication it would go on and complete. Later, these mutants were used to great effect by other people to identify the genes. By using extracts of the mutants and complementing them, many new functions were bio-chemically purified. New DNA polymerases were discovered, and a large number of co-factors that were required for DNA replication were identified and purified. Arthur Kornberg came back to DNA replication with a vengeance once these tools of discovery were provided.

The DNA mutants were an important paradigm for me. No doubt other people have their own examples. But that showed exactly what you had to accomplish in any large-scale genetic experiment. Which was roughly speaking to isolate as many mutants as you can, classify them by complementation so that you've got all the mutants in the same gene, and then study them as deeply as you can in order to find out what they do. And that has flowed through all my work since the early 1960s – just that general approach. You could see this approach working very well with the mutants that affected phage assembly."

Brenner's interest in phage assembly dated back to his early days in Cambridge when, using enzymes and physical methods, he found that he could disassemble phage into various substructures that, under the electron microscope, he identified as "heads" and "sheaths" and "tails". Now genetics was yielding the same substructures.

"Mutants of phage T4 were studied extensively by Edgar and others. They found all the pieces of phage that we had identified when we smashed phage up with enzymes and classified them as cores and sheaths and tails by electron microscopy and negative staining. These people now found that extracts of bacteria infected with these mutant phages that were missing one particular gene could be looked at. And a most remarkable menagerie was discovered. There were mutants with free heads and free tails. There were mutants that formed polyheads. There were polysheaths. And, using all of these, one could now get on to studying interesting questions of phage assembly. The idea that this is really a kit – that you make the parts first and then the parts stick together – really opened up the concept of how you make elaborate cell structures. By this hierarchical self-assembly mode.

But I realised that to understand the complexities of assembling subcellular structures would require more than genetics. One also needed some kind of *in vitro* technique. The genes gave you a means of saturating the genetics, that is, a means of finding all the ways you could break something. You can break it this way or you can break it that way. But to find out what is being broken you needed some other approach. With the phage assembly mutants, people found that they could just mix two extracts. So if they had one mutant that only made heads and one that only made tails, they could mix extracts from the two and the heads and tails would glue together. That's self-assembly with a vengeance!

And you could order all these extracts by mixing them in the right order and seeing whether you got good phage coming out. So you could work out what was an early step and what was a late step in assembly. Did assembly branch into two parts which then united, as indicated by being able to make heads and tails separately? So you had an *in vitro* method of replicating the function. That means you could study the effects of mutations, and the meaning of genes could be determined this way. In DNA replication you could do the same thing. You could take an extract and see if it made DNA. If something was missing from it you could then purify the normal extract and see what you had to add back to replace the missing function. In this way you could get hold of the protein product of the gene and characterise its biochemistry. And of course this type of analysis really opened up the whole definition of the internal machinery of the cell.

Along these lines I had been talking with Francis Crick about what we should do next. An interesting question is whether in the 1960s we were right in thinking that all the main problems of molecular biology had been solved. Our view was that the main outlines *were* known, and that it only remained to populate the various areas of the subject. We were sure that would be done with a vengeance. So when we sat down to discuss the next challenging problems in biology we quickly discarded those in molecular biology that we thought needed immediate solution.

Certainly, at that time, although the outlines were known, nothing was really known about the detailed mechanisms of protein synthesis. And in 1962 there still remained a tremendous task to understand the structure and function of the ribosome; to understand tRNA; to understand how tRNA-activating enzymes worked. You could have written a programme if you wanted to which would involve a huge study of, let us say, the ribosome and the mechanism of protein synthesis. That would involve purifying ribosomes, trying to crystallise them, getting all their protein components, sequencing all the proteins, getting all the tRNAs, separating them, finding all the activating enzymes, and reducing it then to the molecular level. But we thought we didn't want to do that. Even though our institute at that point had the capability of doing it.

Of course, one of the remarkable things about science is that routine work itself generates its own important problems, which you don't see as you stand on the brink, or on the edge, or on the transition point as science goes 'from its heroic period into its classic period', as Gunther Stent used to say. Which is, of course, exactly where molecular biology stood in about 1961. There were no longer great heroes who were evangelists bringing a new message. Now the church was admitting everybody and everybody was becoming converted. I mean, being an early Christian must have been exciting. But to be one later is boring because everybody's converted. The only thing about being an old Jesuit in the church is that you know what's wrong with the church basically, which the new converts don't! But it's important to keep quiet about this in the early stages of building up the church! So I think we were quite right, if arrogant, to say that for us that wasn't the sort of thing we wanted to do.

One of the things that one had always been interested in, since I came from the study of animal cells and Francis had a bit of a cell biology background himself, was to know something about higher organisms. Both of us were interested in the nervous system. I'd spent quite a lot of my youth working in it. But of course it was intractable at that stage. What I thought was, 'We now have all these powerful genetic tools. Can't we use them to approach more complex problems?'"

7
The challenge of
higher organisms

The excitement in the years immediately following the discovery of the structure of
DNA and the unravelling of the genetic code settled, for some scientists at least, into
something of an anticlimax.

"There was, at that time, a feeling that it was essentially all over. This was about
the time that Gunther Stent wrote a famous paper – I forget its title – but it used
to be jokingly called by some of us 'The end of molecular biology'.[1] It was part of
a more general thing of Gunther's which was basically about the end of everything! But I felt that one had to go on to new problems that were challenging. My
view essentially was that we had to go back to the problems that faced Thomas
Morgan, which I discussed earlier [see Chapter 2]. When Morgan, an embryolo-

---

1.   Stent G. **Molecular biology and metaphysics.** *Nature* 1974; **248:**779–781.

gist, discovered that he'd come to the end of what he could do with classical embryological techniques he turned to genetics. I like to call this 'Morgan's genetic deviation', because he thought that in genetics he would learn something new – find a different approach to developmental biology, which he felt had reached a dead end. So he established the fruit fly *Drosophila* as a experimental organism. And of course *Drosophila* became very famous. Similarly, I felt that in a sense I had come to the end of my own 'genetic deviation' and that one had to go back to the problems of biology that had been left behind, like development and differentiation and how genetic programmes are implemented in complex organisms.

But when one discussed development one couldn't really tackle it. One could say 'I'm *interested* in development', or 'I'm *interested* in the nervous system', but nobody actually knew how to do it. The classical technology – if I can put it that way – of development was essentially to cut and splice. You took a piece out of an embryo at one part and you moved it to another part. And you noted whether it changed or it didn't change. If it altered, that is, it took up the properties of its new environment, then we said that it had been 'regulated' and that the change wasn't predetermined. So a whole new language was developed, which I can remember reading about in the 1940s: reading Needham's book *Biochemistry and Morphogenesis* with Joe Gillman and being totally submerged in detailed discussions on the difference between esoteric terms – things like 'evocation' and 'induction' [see Chapter 1, footnote 4]. It was tremendously hard to discover whether 'induction' and 'evocation' were really two different things. We had no other approach then but to cut and splice.

I would say that the classical biochemical approach to development had totally fizzled out. There was a huge area of biochemistry in development which simply consisted of assaying enzymes in eggs and in tadpoles. But the connections simply weren't there. There was a lot of what I would call theoretical work: a few books written by Waddington on organisers and genes. But none of this had any body. It lacked a material content and was simply verbalising our ignorance.

Once we had genes and we knew what they were and we knew that genes made proteins, that just said, 'Well, let's get started and look at how genetics or genes will affect our knowledge of embryology.' But nobody seemed to be very interested in connecting up development with the genes. There was a complete gap between these. When people began to think about this, and began to think in what sense genes could be considered the units of development, it became clear that this was really a nonsensical issue. The units of development are cells. And our job was to ask how genes get hold of cells, if I can put it in that way, because the way the genes get through to the developmental process, and indeed to all the complex phenotypes of organisms, is to regulate the construction machinery of the cell.

If one takes the extreme view that one would like to compute an entire organism from its genome, one has to first understand what one might call the 'principle of construction'. For example, one can look at the head of a virus and one can see that it's a perfect icosahedron. We know that's genetically determined because it's inherited. What we want to know is how is the equation for an icosahedron written in the DNA? We know how such an equation can be written on the back of a package of Corn Flakes. It says, 'Cut here, bend there, glue here and you can fold it all up into this icosahedron.' Similarly, viral icosahedrons are made out of molecules of proteins packing together in a special way. So if we were to unravel all of the structure we would find that the 'equation' for a viral icosahedron is written in little bits and pieces in the genome – in a little sequence of amino acids here, and another little bit there. But we could not disentangle this *a priori* unless we understood the 'principle of construction'.

When we say that the little ducks that follow Konrad Lorenz around are pro-grammed to do so, we don't mean that in the DNA it says, 'Follow Dr Lorenz around.' You have to know the genes and how they work in cells, and how cells build a nervous system, and how the nervous system has capacities for learning. *That's* the way that the genes specify, 'Follow Dr. Lorenz around.' Of course every-body knew that differentiation – that is, how cells came to be different from each other while ostensibly carrying the same genetic information – was another impor-tant problem. The grand paper[2] of Jacob and Monod that explained the basic process of regulating gene expression, at least in bacteria, really gave you a means for seeing this. You could get different types of cells simply by turning off certain genes and turning on certain genes. In fact, Gunther Stent wrote that, as far as he was concerned, embryology or development was a solved problem; it wasn't inter-esting for the simple reason that Jacob and Monod had already told us what to do. But as in all biology the more general the theory, the more vacuous it is. If you sim-ply say, 'Development is just a matter of turning the right genes on in the right place at the right time and that's the answer', that's absolutely true. But it's absolutely useless because somewhere deep down what we'd really like to do is to actually go and make a mouse – build a mouse. Of course no one will build a *real* mouse, but we'd like to be able to make a *gedanken* (imaginary) mouse.

The questions that I think the biologist must ask are threefold. How does it get

2.   Jacob F and Monod J. **Genetic regulatory mechanisms in the synthesis of proteins.** *J Mol Biol* 1961; **3**:318–356.

built? How does it work? How did it get that way? These are the questions of development in the broadest sense. The physiological question must be asked first. But the last question, the question of evolution, I think is the most interesting of these. And since all of this is written in some sense in the genes, that makes genetics the master science of biology. In fact, it's the only science and all the others are just ways of getting to understand what genes do. I say that because that's what evolution must change; that's the material that evolution has to work on. And that's what we finally have to try to understand at the end of the day, or year, or century, or whenever it is.

So I had these ideas that what I wanted to understand was how the genes build an organism – development. In particular, development of the nervous system, because that was the most complicated of all the things. In fact when people asked 'Why do you want to work on the nervous system? Why don't you choose something simpler first, like the big toe or something like that?' I said that I wanted to work on the nervous system because it became absolutely clear to me that no simple hypothesis would account for what that is. My great fear was that everything would finally be explicable by β-galactosidase – by Jacob–Monod theories. There'd be a repressor and you'd take off the repressor and this thing would be induced and that's the way you would get it.

What I wanted was a problem that was so difficult that in fact it wouldn't be so easily explained. The nervous system offered this possibility simply because not only did you have to have cells in the right place, but they had to wire up together accurately. It is the wiring problem of the nervous system, where things grow for very long distances and hook up at the end of the day – at the end of their journeys – with the right cell target, that seemed that you would need very special explanations for, that could not be accounted for in simple terms. And so this is really what one wanted to know."

Many of the central figures in the heyday of molecular biology turned to the brain or the nervous system as their next major challenge. This is true not only of Brenner, but also of Crick, Benzer and several others. The brain is surrounded by an almost irresistible mystique, and unlocking its secrets offers the possibility of uncovering some undreamt of new paradigm in biology. So it is not surprising that understanding the brain, the most formidable challenge in biology, is the most inviting of problems to many scientists. However, despite the formidable intellectual forces that have been ranged against it, the higher functions of the brain, such as cognition, memory, emotion and consciousness, remain unexplained at any sort of fundamental biological level, let alone at the molecular level.

"One of the discussions we had during this time was to try to decompose the complexity of higher organisms into a set of subsidiary problems and tackle each one. There'd be problems of how cells move; that clearly happens in higher organism; cells move around. There'd be problems of how cells grow. There'd be problems of the polarity of cells, which in my mind is still *the* essential problem; in the sense that cells move in one direction and not in another, grow in one direction, or face the world from one side of themselves and not the other. How was all of this polarity established?

In 1965 I played around with *Caulobacter*. *Caulobacter* is a bacterium with a very interesting life cycle, which involves polar growth. One side of the bacterium is different from the other. One side carries a stalk to which the bacterium attaches. When it divides, one of the daughter cells makes a flagellum – a tail – and the other makes a stalk again. So one has to ask how does this bacterium know which is its left side and which is its right side? I also played around with a wonderful bacterium called *Tetramitus* which grows as a square-shaped colony. This means that successive divisions are polarised at right angles to each other."

And then, of course, there were questions of how you turned on all the different genes in an organism that distinguish a neurone from a liver cell. How do things get to be like that? Maybe differentiation could be studied separately from development – taken out of the context of development. So I began to look around for examples which, because of a favourable biological history of that species, might show this in some exaggerated or isolated form. That has been something I've always done, because I think that there is such diversity in living forms that you can always find a special case that aids you with your experiments.

There are classic examples of this. *Acetabularia*, which is an alga, is so big that you can actually suck the contents out of the cell and analyse them, and feel certain that you are still looking at the same process. Where could one find cases in which the exemplar would be such that it would show essentially the same process that you found inside a living organism and that enabled you to investigate it more readily?

I can remember that I was ill one day, and I asked my wife to get me a book on protozoa which I'd phoned in to Heffer's, the booksellers in Cambridge. I had looked at a lot of protozoa during my youth when I was interested in microscopy. I had cultures of *Paramecium* on my lab bench in South Africa and I thought protozoa might be interesting. I started to read very extensively to add to my previous knowledge over the whole of biology. I read entire textbooks of zoology and botany; followed up very specific organisms and traced very special organisms. In protozoa I had known that *Paramecium* was an object of genetic study. *Tetrahymena*, which was another protozoan, had been studied. People had started to do genetic crosses with them. And I also noted that there was a very interesting organism called *Naegleria* which underwent an amoeba–flagellate transformation. And I toyed with the idea that, since one could propagate the amoeba, it would be nice if one could isolate mutants that didn't undergo the transformation to the flagellate form. Then, in the fullness of time, one could find all the genes that were involved in flagella formation. That would be a good way to study differentiation and what turns it on in this case.

I became very interested in cell counting systems. How do organisms know how to count numbers of cells? For example, I was tremendously impressed by reading that the fly *Sciara* has supernumerary chromosomes which it gets rid of in all but two cells at the sixteen-cell stage. So one can ask, 'How does it know when it's got exactly sixteen cells?' There must be some sort of cell counting thing.

In the course of my reading I came across the Micrometazoa. These are little animals which are extremely interesting. There are two kinds that I got interested in. One were rotifers, which I'd known as an amateur microscopist. I actually went out to one of the ponds outside Cambridge to get a culture of rotifers. And these looked very exciting. They weren't single cells; they were collections of cells. They had sexual cycles and they had intestines and they had muscles and they were really small animals. I looked very carefully at the rotifers and, although I played around with them a lot (they were extremely beautiful to look at), they had impossibly slow sexual cycles! They had cycles such that the females grew parthenogenetically. This is an organism that treats the male sex with great disrespect because the male is produced simply to fertilise females! It has no feeding organs. Feeding organs are a waste of time because it's going to die anyway! So these males are simply there to exchange genes between the populations and to make sure that the mix that greets the next season is such that nature can select once again for the best for that season. But these beasts had a very complex life cycle. I also found that they were very irritating because they lived in three dimensions – they swam around in water. I wanted an organism with a two-dimensional world, like bacteria, which can live on the surface of a petri dish.

I did all of these experiments with my own hands for the simple reason that I loved the cultivation of organisms. I just loved growing all these strange bacteria and other things! I've always found it interesting to bring projects to the stage that other people can take them over and develop all the little tricks."

But after a number of excursions to the wilder shores of zoology, Brenner came to the conclusion that many of these models were not in fact models of anything useful except themselves.

"During this time I invented a new class of organisms! In addition to the vertebrates and invertebrates I thought that there were also pervertebrates. These were organisms that were thought to be like others, but were simply models of themselves. Like slime moulds – much to the anger of the people who worked with this organism!

One of the things that ran through all of our work at this time, and which I think came from my background of always having a microscope around, was always having a look at things. I called this HAL biology – Have A Look biology! What's the use of doing a lot of biochemistry if you can simply see what's happening? I remember that many years ago when I was working with bacteria, Sol Spiegelman had claimed that when he added ribonuclease to bacterial protoplasts they stopped making protein. He took this as evidence that RNA was involved in protein synthesis. But I always looked at the protoplasts under the microscope and when I added ribonuclease they disappeared. Which of course was very good reason why they stopped making proteins. They stopped doing everything!

During the course of all this reading I came across the nematodes, which are tiny worms. These looked far more promising. The more I read about them the more I became totally excited by them, and decided that this is the organism that I would go for. So I started to isolate nematodes from nature to find the best one. We knew from the literature that they had a small number of cells and they had rapid growth, and as it turned out, there were the right possibilities for sexuality in order to do genetic experiments. Now we knew about some really classic experiments done in the early part of the century by [Richard] Goldschmidt,[3] who had worked on the nervous system of *Ascaris*. He produced a very remarkable set of papers. If you read about his life you'll find that he did these when he was studying zoology as a student. He made dissections of *Ascaris*, which is a very large parasitic nematode, mainly of pigs, and found that he could describe the entire nervous system. It had just a few hundred cells. And he could also describe all the cellular connections.

When I went to look at the journal *Jahrbuch der Zoologie*, where all this was published, in the Cambridge University Library, I found the pages uncut. So I was

---

3. Richard Goldschmidt (1878–1958). German embryologist, emigrated to the United States and worked there for the latter part of his life.

absolutely certain that no one had read that journal until I opened it in the early 1960s. That means it had been there for at least fifty years. So I said to myself, 'Well, the nematode is an organism which must have a wiring diagram for its brain. So it should be possible to ask whether all organisms have the same wiring diagram if they have the same genes. Then we could say which genes specified wiring diagrams.' The conceptual layout was very clear in my mind. We would determine the wiring diagram of the nervous system of an animal, a nematode. At the same time we would make mutations and ask what alterations these caused in the wiring diagram and thereby relate the structure to genetics. And then, if you knew the structure of the nervous system, the anatomy, and how it is genetically programmed, you could begin to ask questions about how it worked.

My good friend and colleague Seymour Benzer had also decided to drop phage and move to higher organisms. He decided to work on *Drosophila* and he too had this idea of genetic dissection, which is to take a phenotype, find out how many ways there are of breaking it by making mutants, and in this way identify all the genes that specify the phenotype. But I believed that you could not relate the genes to function in higher organisms that simply. I remember pictures of Konrad Lorenz being followed around by his ducks. And I always wanted to know if there was a gene, so to speak, to put the left foot forward, followed by another gene that said, 'And having done that put the right foot forward'. In other words, were there units of behaviour and did they map onto the genetic programme as such? Indeed, if one thinks of the entire complex organism one could ask, 'What are *all* the units of this organism that might possibly be mapped genetically?' Are there genes for the liver, so to speak, that are distinct from genes for the kidney?

I decided that at least for the brain, there were two distinct issues in this process. One question is, 'How do you build the nervous system?' Now that's what the genes do. But then you also have to ask, 'How does the nervous system work to generate behaviour?' The important idea here is exactly the one that we had in the molecular biology of bacteriophage. You can't understand how the gene corresponds to the phenotype without understanding the paradigm of construction between them – the 'construction paradigm'. Once you understand that phage are put together by molecules [assembling] into sub-assemblies and that these sub-assemblies are then glued together to make a phage, you can understand how the genes correspond to this geometrical structure. The same must be true of higher organisms. You have to separate the construction issue – the developmental issue, the building issue – from that of function. The two are interlocked, because clearly what organisms do is an output from the machines that they possess to do things with. And what machines have to do things with is an output of their genes.

Well, all this analysis told me that from a genetic point of view the most important question to ask first was how genes build nervous systems. You know, I could never understand why people had these endless arguments in the field of behavioural genetics, which was very popular in the early 1960s; arguments about genes and intelligence, for example, which aroused tremendous anger. People said things like 'It's just impossible that genes specify intelligence.' Of course genes affect intelligence, in the sense that they are needed to build your brain. It's not a question of philosophy or belief. It's a question of what it is and how it works! And the whole constraint of this is that everything has to be produced by evolution. Intelligence had to be produced by evolution. Presumably unintelligent people didn't survive in the early days. They couldn't cope with the environment, so they were eliminated. Once you recognise that everything comes through this evolutionary sieve, through this filter, and that the filter has to work with genes, you can see how all of these things are interrelated. And the one thing that we can do in a laboratory is to dissect these – separate all these issues and define them in this way. The nematode seemed to me to be the best way of doing this, and I therefore started what is now known as the *C. elegans* project."

Brenner had chosen the tiny soil nematode Caenorhabditis elegans *as his experimental subject. He decided that, in order to have recognisable phenotypes to identify mutants in the wiring of the* C. elegans *nervous system, he needed to know the entire cellular anatomy of the nervous system of this worm in detail. He wanted to know which specific cell was joined to which other specific cell. Such a detailed cellular map of the brain could not be identified by conventional microscopy. So he turned to the electron microscope.*

"If I wanted to be sure which cell was joined to which other cell I would have to look at individual cell membranes. An electron microscope can resolve cell membranes. In essence what we needed to do was three-dimensional electron microscopy. How were we going to do that? In a very classic mode! As a student in South Africa I had reconstructed the brain of *Galago* by serial sectioning using collodion sections. By tracing these on paper and transferring these to slices of wax, I actually made a three-dimensional model of this brain in wax with all the holes in it, and you could open it up and look inside.

So I decided that we'd have to do something like that. We'd have to cut serial sections and we'd have to go from one section to the next and trace it. Now the electron microscope is extremely powerful, but it has a very tiny 'window'. You can only look at a small piece of anything at a time. This meant that for one to do this on a whole organism we would have to get something that was very, very small in order to fit it into the 'window' of the electron microscope. And in fact, this was the predominant condition that forced us to the Micrometazoa. The small size of this nematode – the adult is only one millimetre in length and about forty microns in cross section, and the larvae of course are much smaller – meant that these could fit well into the 'window' of the electron microscope.

I felt that we needed a *complete* wiring diagram of the brain because modellers are always confronted by sceptics. So if you explain to the sceptic, 'I have modelled this behaviour and we've got this oscillator which interacts with this and it's coupled in this way and it does this', and he says, 'That's very nice, but how do you know there isn't another wire which goes from this point, you know, goes right around the back and comes in at the side again?', you need to be able to say, 'There are no more wires. We know all the wires.' So you must saturate this kind of database, if you like, so that nothing can be added to it."

And so the general experimental plan evolved. Brenner decided to physically map the presence and location of every cell in the nervous system of the nematode C. elegans. *The idea was then to generate mutant worms with perturbations in nervous system function, as evidenced by some sort of observable behavioural phenotype such as abnormal locomotion, or feeding behaviour, and find out which cells in the nervous system were affected in these mutants and which genes were mutated in these cells. This was the new 'grand scheme'.*

"Let's get the structure of the nervous system and then we can solve the problem of behaviour. Because we can make perturbations, we can do experiments. That,

I thought, is the general way to approach this. So now you had to get down and do the work! I was very fortunate that Lord Rothschild [Victor Rothschild] was a good friend of mine at that time. I used to drink martinis with him every weekend! He was, for many years, a scientist in the Zoology Department at Cambridge, and when he stopped doing science he had a technician, Nicol Thompson, who had worked for him for a long time and for whom he was anxious to find a job. So he talked to me about this and I thought that this would be ideal because Nicol was a highly trained electron microscopist. We had a lot of problems because Nicol didn't have a higher education let alone school education, having been born in a rural village in Scotland. This was in the days when people began to worry about qualifications, which I think is complete nonsense! So of course I had a lot of arguments with administrators. But we finally got Nicol a decent appointment and he began to tackle the problem of these little beasts.

I had a lot of nematodes because I was trying to find out which grew best. I wanted to make temperature-sensitive mutants. So I thought, 'What if we get nematodes from the equator?' Surely they must be used to 37°C and then we could get mutants that grow at lower temperatures and we could do the conditional-lethality thing more easily. So I talked with the Director of Research for Shell Oil, and we took a map of the world and looked at where all the oil facilities are around the world. There were a lot of them on the equator, plus or minus 5. Oil in Nigeria, Malaysia, South America. So through him it was arranged that everybody would bring back some soil dug up from outside the airport. I just filtered them, stuck them on agar plates with bacteria as their food and watched them grow! We also collected a large number from around Cambridge. Every time that someone went on holiday I said, 'Bring back some soil!'

We certainly got over sixty strains and these were looked at very quickly for how well they grew and whether they could be cut for electron microscopy and so on. We went through a lot of these and some were just totally awful. So they wouldn't cut or they wouldn't fix properly. Others had impossible sex lives – they wouldn't grow well. But we collected a lot of interesting comparative data. The sections we did were straight through the head. The head of a nematode contains a tremendous array of sensory organs, all of which are rather beautiful, and all of which are enclosed in something the size of a single human red blood cell.

Eventually it turned out that a very famous nematode called *Caenorhabditis elegans* [*C. elegans*] was the one that worked best for us. There was a man called Doherty in the United States at Berkeley who was interested in nematodes. He worked in the Department of Nutrition and was interested in what nematodes ate. Now everybody knew that nematodes ate either other nematodes or bacteria or fungi. But he was interested in growing them in a defined liquid medium. That was his primary work, and he had reduced a culture to a whole lot of amino acids and vitamins. There were tremendously complex things in it like horse liver extract. This was very pertinent for me because one of the things I was interested in was to see if I get nutritional mutants of nematodes, because I felt that if we could get our hands on a biosynthetic gene to start with we'd learn how to isolate nematode genes and proteins.

I also liked *C. elegans* very much because it had a beautiful sex life. It is what is called a self-fertilising hermaphrodite. First the gonad develops into a testis and then stops and switches to make oocytes. Then these fertilise each other. So each animal is the result of a cross of itself with itself. There's no better in-breeding than to cross yourself with yourself all the time! So this animal had the property of being completely isogenic because each animal had a uniform genetic constitution: it was a clone, so to speak. Furthermore, when you made mutants these would segregate in the cross of that animal in Mendelian proportions.

Also these nematodes have occasional males which crop up in cultures and you can use these males to move genes from one animal to another. That gave you the whole basis of doing genetics. They also had a very rapid life cycle and they lived on bacteria, and it looked as though they might be axenised [conditioned to grow on defined medium]. So after some time of looking at lots and lots of other worms, we alighted on *C. elegans*.

One of the things that you want when you're doing a lot of genetics is to be able to store clones of these animals. With *E. coli* it was very easy. We just froze them in glycerol, and just put them away like that. So you can keep this tremendous inventory of different clones. It's one of the databases geneticists want in order to be able to locate mutants quickly. Phage were perfect. You just kept them in little bottles, a drop or two was enough. So it doesn't take much room. Of course if you work with mice you've got to keep on breeding them! They're very hard to store. So we wanted some way of storing these worms. We didn't want to keep on propagating them because that becomes an enormous labour. Fortunately it was discovered by John Sulston in the lab – I was doing these experiments as well and I hadn't had much luck – that you can freeze nematodes. There were lots of papers on how you did this with people. But we hadn't heard of any one who'd actually been successfully thawed, you see! Anyway, by slow freezing, about a degree a minute, you could in fact preserve these animals and thaw them and have them come alive. That was signal advantage.

We also found, very quickly, that they are susceptible to mutagenesis by a compound called ethylmethanesulphonate [EMS]. Indeed, you could mutate their genes at about the same frequency as you could mutate the genes of the *E. coli* bacteria that accompanied them. And that enabled us to get the whole of the genetics under way. The first mutant was isolated in 1967. It was called E1. It's a famous mutant. The E stands for EMS. Later the E stood for mutants that were isolated in Cambridge. Each mutant was given a file and into that file went everything and anything that had to do with that mutant. There are several hundred such files now on record in the Laboratory of Molecular Biology, and there's quite a history embodied in them.

So we pushed ahead on a number of things simultaneously, and it's the sort of thing that I like to do, to have lots of things to do so that if one gets stuck you can go on with the other thing. We started to master the techniques of serial sectioning. And then there was the selecting of mutants. People asked 'How do you pick behavioural mutants?' Well, you have a whole lot of nematodes and some of them are mutants and some of them are not. And anything that looked funny or different in any way, you picked and put on a little petri dish by itself. If its children showed the same difference then it was a mutant, because it was inherited. Now you had to cross it and make sure you could segregate the mutant in one quarter of the population.

In our first experiment we only got two mutants. With the second one we got ten and with the third we got about thirty to forty, which was exactly where it plateaus from each batch of plates that you can handle in a cycle. And then you started to find repeats. Then we started to work on drugs. I got hold of every drug capable of curing nematodes – you know, things they fed to cattle or pigs to cure them of the worm, or sprayed on plants and so on. We found that some of these paralysed the nematodes. There's a very good one called tetramisole that paralysed nematodes. I found I could get resistant mutants to this. And we developed techniques for selecting rare behavioural mutants by taking a petri dish and putting a few thousand nematodes on one side of it and some bacteria on the other side. Of course the nematodes can smell the bacteria and know they've got to get there, but only the ones that can move get there efficiently. So we had very selective screens. All of this then began to build up and began to attract other people."

In typical Brenner style, the famous C. elegans *project was launched in many simultaneous directions. This worm rapidly became one of the established model systems for the genetics and biology of multicellular organisms. Eventually, the* C. elegans *genome was selected as one of the eukaryotic genomes to be incorporated into the international gene sequencing venture – the Genome Projects. At about this time Crick was also developing a serious interest in cell biology, and he and Brenner formed a new Unit of Cell Biology in the MRC Laboratories.*

"Our idea was to import as many people as we could get hold of to work in this field. There were a large number of English people in America in different labs and one of the things we did was to bring some of them back. The idea was that they could work on anything they liked provided it had something to do with these new problems of development or how cells perform in development. People asked us what the qualifications were for them to come back and we said, 'Just interest in the subject!' Having this rather flexible style, we attracted people from all kinds of backgrounds.

During this period, Francis had become very interested in gradients. It was one of the things that Lewis Wolpert had put forward as a new idea in embryology. That cells took up their characteristics from their positions in a gradient field. This idea of Lewis's was very novel, but he didn't get much interest in it. I can remember finding him in Woods Hole in the late 1960s very depressed, saying that he'd given these lectures and no one paid any attention to him. At that time I was also teaching in Woods Hole and I can remember people discussing questions like, 'Is development a state or a process?' So I asked them, 'Do you know the difference between laid-back and mellowing out?' Some people may remember these great terms from the 1960s! And of course that's exactly the difference between a state and a process. Mellowing is a process and laid-back is a state. By mellowing out you hope to reach the laid-back state! But the point is that Francis got interested in much of this sort of thing. He was especially interested in gradients, in the relative sizes of things, and noticed that things were scaled about to what you would expect from a diffusion gradient. So he began to do calculations on this and began to interest people in these experiments.

This was one of the great successes of the Laboratory of Molecular Biology. That you could come from any background and, if you were interested in the actual problem and in how to resolve it, you qualified to get in. For example, Graham Mitchison wrote to me. He was an algebraic topologist. His only contact with biology I suppose was because his uncle Avrion Mitchison was an immunologist. And we said, 'Okay, come and work on development and these gradients.' John Sulston was an organic chemist by background. John White was an engineer. So we had a group of people working over a wide range of biology, including the new nematode work. Francis had become interested in vision and was deep in reading David Hubel and Torsten Wiesel's papers. It was during this time that we made contact with David Marr, who was a young mathematician. And we gave him a job in the lab simply because he was working on something interesting.

I've always found that the best people to push science forward are those who come from outside it. Maybe that's the same in culture as well. The emigrés are always the best people to make the new discoveries! So when someone said to me once 'What is the nature of the organisation in your laboratory?', I could only think of one answer, which was, 'Loose gangs!' There were just groups of people who got together and whose aim was to push the subject forward. And that is how the whole new work developed."

8
How to do molecular biology in *C. elegans*

"During this time [the 1960s and 1970s] the lab in Cambridge was absolutely the most marvellous place to work in, because one would do a different thing almost every hour. I had an office which l shared with Francis. I had shared this office with him since I came to Cambridge. What we did in the new lab was to equip it with blackboards. We still liked simple chalk and blackboards. We had one blackboard in our old little office and we acquired lots of them now. And on these blackboards we would meet, often every day, and talk about anything and everything. We would talk about an experimental result and ask, 'What could this possibly mean?' Or Francis would tell me he'd just read this paper: these were his views about it. What is very interesting is that we pursued very divergent scientific paths, but we still came together for these discussions.

The Americans in our lab always wanted journal clubs or formal discussion groups. I've never been in favour of this. But I told them that if they wanted to, they could organise this sort of thing for themselves. For a year I did form something facetiously called the S[ydney] B[renner] Educational Society, in which everybody was informed with five minutes notice that they had to tell me what they were doing, to educate me. This again wasn't liked by the Americans, who required time for preparation of what they had to say. But it seemed to me that if you had to prepare anything on what you were doing at the moment you'd better get worried, because it meant you really didn't know what you were doing!

The other very informal discussion group was known as the 'Saturday morning coffee'. We congregated in the kitchen, the sterilising kitchen on the second floor, where we made coffee on a Saturday morning. People came from all over the lab and we would discuss everything: molecular structure, embryology, psychology, sometimes politics. Just anything! There were many, many interesting discussions held there.

I feel that this kind of ongoing conversation is so important to science. It's important to me personally because I'm not the sort of person who likes to think in isolation. There are a number of people I know who can go away and cook up a whole theory and then come back and do it. I don't. To me a lot of what's beneficial in science is from conversation. Because when an idea forms in my mind it's usually at least fifty percent wrong the first time it appears. And it's only in playing with it, if I can call it that, that you can refine it and see what's essential in it. I believe that sort of interaction is one of the great joys of science. Suddenly saying, 'Gee, you know, I actually got it wrong the first time, but now I can see it.' And of course the other real joy is to be able to convert that into an experiment and then go and do the experiment and get the answer.

I say this because the whole of the *C. elegans* project wasn't anything like the science I'd done earlier. With the science I'd done earlier, I'd come in at the right time. So you could formulate the questions, go and do an experiment, and if not that day, then at least the next day you would know the answer. The *C. elegans* project was very much more strategic. In fact it took a long time to mature, and I don't think we could have done it in an environment that required short-term justification for anything. This was a feature of science in Britain in the 1960s. Having accomplished quite a lot and got yourself good marks for it, you were kind of given a blanker cheque than most other people got. In fact, the great trick was to foster what I called the 'horse and cart paradox'. What you wanted to do is to have the people sitting in the driving seat believe that they were steering it. Whereas, of course, the horse knows where to go and is just taking the cart where he wants to. So I think that the Medical Research Council [MRC] who financed all the work – because there had been so many glorious things done – just said 'Well, you know, they can't go too far wrong.' And being able to work without this endless justification that is so common today, and which I feel is completely stifling to creative work in science, made that subject [the *C. elegans* project]. That and the fact that there were a lot of young people willing to gamble on it. A lot of Americans came to the lab. Some of them came to work on transfer RNA and switched half way. From the 1970s on, many people joined the project.

One of the most interesting things that happened is the love affair with computers that got consummated during this period. We needed to record an enormous amount of information on the reconstruction of the nervous system. We wondered a lot how this could be done and of course came to the conclusion that we should use a computer to help us. This was in the mid 1960s, and in those days biologists were, in general, very antagonistic to computers. They thought that anybody interested in computing was choosing an easy way out of a responsible job. In other words, if you didn't work at the bench you weren't worth anything!

Graham Mitchison was a mathematician, and so was David Marr. And John White was an engineer. So we asked the MRC for our own computer to help us with this work. But in those days computing was only done in a computing centre, and the idea that you would have a dedicated machine devoted to one kind of project was still very rare indeed. And certainly organisations like the MRC hadn't come up with this. They wanted to know how many operators we'd have, and how many shifts we'd run, and so on. There was this idea that because computers were very expensive one had to use them every moment. We tried to tell them that we didn't want to do computing that way. That computers should be the servants not the masters! That's when I invented the term 'ad hoc', which stands for 'hands on computing!' And of course in those days if you asked for an American machine you never got it. I remember that we did pursue the possibility of buying a used computer. This the MRC thought was rather to be suspected. I mean no good organisation bought a second-hand computer!

I had been very impressed by what I'd seen at MIT in the artificial intelligence programme, where my friend from South Africa, Seymour Papert, was now a professor. I could see that computers would not only become standard laboratory tools, but in fact they would constitute the essence of what we would be doing in biological research in the future. So a suitable English-made computer, in fact a rather advanced machine called the Modular I, was finally located and transported to the MRC Laboratories in Cambridge and housed in shell space in the new building. This was the shell of a building that was just concrete. The MRC told us that the building could not be used to expand the work of people already there, but to bring new work in. Which I think is a very healthy idea when you are building an institute.

It was the most wonderful building I've ever worked in. There were no services except the electrical services, which we led in on open wires on the floor. So we essentially had this sort of vast hall with the computer sitting in the middle and acres of space to enjoy ourselves with. We needed acres of space because in those days the computer had no means of doing anything except an assembler program. There was no high-level language programmed for it, and all input and output was done on paper tape. I can remember lying on the floor with tons of paper tape unwound, editing individual punched holes.

It was a most interesting period in the sense that one got down to the actual essence of computing. So one of the things that I did was to teach myself computing thoroughly. David and John and Graham and I became so skilled that we thought nothing of writing operating systems for this machine. And by thinking about computers, by thinking about other complex objects and how one would try to account for them, I laid the ground for most of the way that I now view complex biological systems. I think increasingly everybody else will have to view them in this way. Which is of course a return to the old von Neumann paradigm: if you can't compute it you can't understand it!

I shall never forget that I was once asked to meet a man who was the President of the British Computing Society. I said 'Sure', and he came up and we had lunch together in Cambridge. He said to me, 'I've been dying to meet you because we're interested in writing programs for banks. What we'd like to know is how biological systems perform all these complicated things? Maybe there are some clues for us for programming.' And I replied, 'You know, I'm really delighted to meet *you* because I'm interested in how these biological systems do all these complex things, and I thought that if I study some complex programs for banks I would get some clues to explaining this.' So we departed with great mutual ignorance!"

During this period Brenner became interested at a theoretical level in the molecular basis of neuronal wiring in the brain. His interest stemmed from experiments by Marcus Jacobson and others who showed the remarkable specificity of the regeneration of neuronal wiring between retina and tectum in lower vertebrates. An interesting theory that could account for this – called the chemo-affinity theory – had been proposed by Roger Sperry.

"What he [Sperry] proposed was that each recipient cell in a neuronal connection had a specific receptor molecule, and each donor cell in the connection had a specific ligand. If these molecules matched, the two nerve cells would wire up. So you had to have these matching sets which had to meet. If one thinks about this it becomes obvious that one would need a very large number of specific chemical molecules. But this was not really a problem because everyone knew that a similar thing happens in the immune system in generating antibodies. In fact, Leo Szilard wrote a theoretical paper about how the nervous system might be wired by this form of chemical recognition and, what is more, he used the paradigm of the immune system as a model for learning and memory.

This idea that every connection, so to speak, in the nervous system would be encoded by a specific molecular interaction gave rise to a lot of problems. Jacobson wrote a paper in which he argued that it was impossible, for the simple reason that there weren't enough genes in the genome. He calculated the number of synapses in the nervous system and showed that this was vastly in excess of the number of base pairs in the DNA, let alone genes. But that was a rather naïve analysis because it strongly underestimated the power of combinatorics. That is, if you take a number of elementary events and you repeat them in various ways you can get enormous computation power out of it. I was able to show, just as an exercise to suit myself, that I could specify a theoretical retina with about 10 million specific chemicals, or combinations of chemicals, by using just 112 genes.

I didn't believe in it [this theoretical outcome], because it assumed that prime numbers existed in nature. That's one of the reasons I didn't believe in it. Another reason is that I calculated how long it would take to do – because it involved one cell telling another cell to turn on a gene, and then it would tell its neighbour – and it would take too long.

Theories should always contain some biochemical plausibility. One can do things in a very sophisticated mathematical way. But if in fact it takes seventy years to achieve this in a real biological system it's of no relevance! It's the difference between theories being correct and theories being true. Many theoreticians don't make that difference, but in fact many theories are *correct* in a logical sense, but they're *untrue* because they don't relate to the natural thing we're all interested in!"

The C. elegans *project was a very long-term affair. But eventually the anatomy of the nematode nervous system was completed and the lab moved on.*

"Later, John Sulston did the complete development of the worm, following each cell during development. And of course we had opened up the genetics. That said, by 1972, the first paper published on C. *elegans*[1] just said that we would pursue this. But I knew that one would have to get down to the molecular basis, and it seemed daunting. We hadn't any idea of how many genes were involved or how many proteins were involved. One of the things that I did in the very early days on *C. elegans*, which is part of the first paper we published, was to estimate the number of indispensable genes. I found there were actually relatively few. And since many people believed there would be hundreds of thousands, this was very reassuring. It wasn't believed by anybody! I think that we rather underestimated it because I think there are lots of genes that are not lethal, so to speak, but that are still needed. But nonetheless, the idea that you could build something as complicated as a nematode with, say, 10,000 genes was absolutely not thought possible by many people.

With all of these people and with all this progress, I thought in the early 1970s that we should start to do molecular biology. And that meant isolating gene products. We thought we'd start with something that we knew about. It turned out that a lot of our mutants were paralysed and many of these had defective muscles. That we could see in the electron microscope. Since a muscle, as anybody who eats meat knows, is the major portion of many animals, these proteins are quite abundant. And to a biochemist that's very attractive. So we decided to see whether any of the mutants corresponded to the known structural proteins of muscle such as actin and myosin and tropomyosin and so on.

We developed methods for growing large quantities of nematodes. We grew large fermentors of bacteria and then we threw in the nematodes. They ate all the bacteria and then we would harvest the nematodes. That enabled us to isolate

1.   Brenner S. **The genetics of** *Caenorhabditis elegans*. *Genetics* 1974; **77**:71–94.

reasonable quantities of these proteins and begin the long job of finding out which of the mutants corresponded to them. One of the things we discovered this way is a gene called *unc-54* which controls the expression of the heavy chain of myosin. And another gene called *unc-15* controls the specification of another muscle protein called paramyosin.

I started to look at mutants of the nervous system early on and found that many of these that were not muscle mutants had large deviations in the organisation of their neurones. Of course, what you hoped for was that you could find a very specific difference so that you could identify a process that corresponded to a gene. But all we could really say about most of these mutants is that their nervous system was a mess! Nonetheless, it was interesting to ask how many of them made the same mess and how many made a different mess. In fact we could find various classes of this. We found a number of mutants that made exactly the same mess every time. And we found another mutant [gene] which made different messes in different organisms.

This led us during this time to ask questions like, "Is the genetic program specified to say, 'Build a complete leg', or does it say, 'Build a *sort* of leg'?", and then you have all this tinkering that goes on, which evolution has added, to build a proper leg – an accurate leg? One's guess is the latter scenario. There are probably general leg programmes and then there's a second level that we can call 'refining programmes'.

These two levels of organisation will give you totally different results when you start to break the system apart with mutations. Let's say that an insect has six legs. One programme might specify that you either get six legs or no legs. But another programme might specify that you get *some* legs. So mutants of this programme might give you five legs or four. I don't think this has been carefully studied at all. I think all of these mutations have been very deliberately thrown away by the geneticists. They call them mutants of low penetrance, or low expressivity, or variable phenotypes, or leaky. And they're not studied. I'm fairly certain that these mutants contain a lot of information about how developmental programmes evolved. And as opposed to the point of view that people have now, that you either have six legs or no legs, I think we're going to see that it's very different. Evolution might actually be viewed as taking one step backward and then two steps forward in another direction. That's the sort of thing that I think will eventually emerge as we understand these programmes.

But the core of it, and it worried me all the time, was how on earth would one ever get down to finding the molecules involved in regulation? If there were regulatory proteins and if any of our mutants affected these, how on earth would we actually prove this? If there were proteins like the Jacob–Monod ones, that recognised DNA, and if any of the mutations affected these, how on earth could we actually prove this? Even though the muscle programme was the first approach using molecular biology, it was kind of token molecular biology. It wasn't getting at the essence of the molecular basis of development. Francis and I discussed these questions at great length.

In the early 1970s we both got very interested in the fact that it appeared that higher organisms had more DNA than they should reasonably have to specify what they were doing. It used to be said that scientists could be divided into three classes. There were the physicists, who believed that organisms didn't have enough DNA to do what they thought were very complicated things. There were the smart molecular biologists, who thought that organisms had exactly the right amount of DNA that they needed. And then there were a group of people who were really concerned with what this extra DNA was required for. We were trying very hard to understand whether this extra DNA was just junk in a very general sense, or whether it was concealing some sort of special mechanism. This was one of the things that we discussed eternally on these blackboards in Francis' room. We wondered whether this extra DNA was used for gene regulation. If so, why did you need so much and why didn't we find it in lower organisms? Many of these notions and ideas were written on the blackboard and of course the central part of the board was always erased because one needed more space. So there were things left on the side. My desk faced the blackboard and I would sometimes look at it and say, "What does this word 'dreams' mean?" Which was all that was left of some earlier discussion!

One day Francis came in very excited about a new idea of gene regulation in higher cells. The general idea was that the regulatory elements would have to recognise rather longer stretches of DNA and you couldn't do this with proteins. You'd have to have nucleic acid–nucleic acid recognition. And because you had to have what we would now call many instantiations of this, you would have to have large areas of the genome used for control, for regulation. And that was why there was so much DNA in higher organisms. Francis wrote a paper on this notion based on an axiom he called 'The principle of versatility and recognition by RNA', and deduced everything from this. It was an interesting way of trying to work things out. As I pointed out to him, at least it had the clarity that if the axiom was wrong everything else would have to be wrong!

At the time the thing that I did not like about this, and said so, was that it assumed that there's only a two-value logic in developmental systems. Namely ON or OFF. And if you have to specify that only the ON things are relevant, then you have a great problem of turning everything off in every other case. Suppose you have a hundred different cell types, you have to make a list of genes that are ON or OFF for every case. These lists will be very disjointed. So you'll have to have different ways of regulating combinations. Furthermore, there may be lots of what I've called 'don't care' situations. That is, if a muscle protein that is turned on in a neurone has no effect, there'll be no reason to worry about turning it ON or OFF! You can just leave it.

In fact, there is a remarkable experiment which illustrates this. Someone grafted the eye of a tadpole just above the tail. When the tail shrunk down the eye got positioned just above the cloaca [anus] and it grew there. What was remarkable is that it grew back in one column of the spinal cord and one column only. Now nature didn't have to specify for the retina not to grow in any of these columns, because nature doesn't worry about cases where the eye suddenly occurs above the anus! So it is clear that there could be many 'don't care' situations. Francis and I had many arguments about his sort of thing and these discussions, as you might imagine, went on a lot.

I wrote a paper in which I accounted for the extra DNA as just junk. That wasn't liked very much because people feel very uncomfortable with the idea that a lot of their DNA is of no value! Not to them, not to anybody! But I think that we have to get beyond simple psychology to really appreciate the forces in evolution that determine that junk can be kept or not kept as the case may be. My contribution to the DNA junk subject was simply to differentiate between 'junk' and 'garbage'. Junk is the rubbish you keep and garbage is the rubbish you throw out! So extra DNA by definition cannot be garbage, but only junk. If it were garbage it wouldn't be there!

Well, having reached this stage, in the early 1970s, of extensive analysis of the genetics of this beast [*C. elegans*], an extensive amount of work on the biochemistry beginning, the anatomy going ahead, the development going ahead, the techniques of knocking out neurones by laser ablation and having a way of studying development, one felt that the ship was at sea, but it was very unclear where it was heading. I felt that if we wanted to do things more definitively, which is to get down to the molecular basis, we had to have some new technique.

I had conceived a type of experiment which Francis dissuaded me from doing. This was to see if nematode genes would work in bacteria. I knew that *Bacillus subtilis* was an organism that would accept almost any DNA. So I said, 'If I can get a mutant of *Bacillus subtilis* in, let us say, a glycolytic enzyme, molecular biology had shown us that the glycolytic enzymes were the same throughout the whole of nature. Triosephosphate isomerase from me and *E. coli* and yeast and lobsters are all very similar proteins. So that function should be retained.' So, I reasoned, I should be able to take nematode DNA and see if I could restore a defective gene function in a strictly non-revertible *B. subtilis* mutant. If I got that result then I'd have a handle, so to speak, and I could climb in with other nematode genes and bacterial mutants. This would be a brute force approach to isolating nematode genes.

I had a whole scheme worked out in about 1972 or 1973 to do these huge transformation experiments to identify *C. elegans* genes. Of course we now know that experiment wouldn't have had a hope in hell of working. Not a chance! Zero! For the simple reason that nematode genes have introns in them. The bacterium wouldn't have known what to do with them, apart from all the other barriers to gene transfer – host modification, and so on – that we now know about. So Francis talked me out of it. He was quite right, because I thought it was, you know, the last desperate experiment."

Brenner's ideas were moving in the direction of isolating individual genes from multicellular organisms such as the worm, but standard genetics had no means to do this. He recognised that this next step was required to take the understanding of complex organisms to a new level. His thinking was, in fact, anticipating a coming biological revolution.

"At about that time, Paul Berg [one of the pioneers of gene cloning at Stanford University] came to the lab and asked me for advice on an experiment that he was trying to do with the virus SV40, which was eventually the first genetic engineering experiment reported. And I told him that I thought it was a very interesting experiment, but why not do it with something simpler than SV40, which is a tumour virus? But he didn't really want my opinion on the nature of the experiment. He wanted to know whether he ought to *do* the experiment. Whether it was the ethically *right* thing to do. This was the opening scene of what hit us in the middle of 1974, when all these experiments were reported: the beginnings of genetic manipulation and its problems. But I immediately recognised this would be the way to tackle the genetics of higher organisms and I wanted very much to do it, to clone genes."

9
The evolution of genetics and the genetics of evolution

Brenner's experience with C. elegans *showed that, despite great care in selecting a model organism, getting a hold on the genes and proteins of multicellular eukaryotic organisms was a far greater problem than it had been for bacteria and bacteriophages.*

But just as it seemed that the fervour of molecular biology was beginning to wane, and that modern biology was about to enter its anticipated extended plateau, a revolutionary technology appeared, that of gene cloning and gene manipulation. This potentially offered the means of identifying, isolating, propagating and studying any gene from any organism. Thus, in the mid 1970s, a mere twenty years after the discovery of the structure of DNA, a radically new approach to the genetics of plants and animals became possible for the first time since the development of classical genetics at the beginning of the century. A history of the modern era of genetic manipulation might well be called 'The ninth day of creation', to paraphrase Judson, [see footnote 10, Chapter 2].

The development of gene cloning was the result of several more-or-less simultaneous discoveries in the late 1960s and early 1970s. First was the discovery of a class of bacterial enzymes – the restriction enzymes – that can cut DNA, any DNA, in unique places and hence into unique pieces. These enzymes evolved to assist bacteria in their struggle for survival by recognising and cutting up foreign DNA, especially that of invading bacteriophages, and are called restriction enzymes, because they restrict the ability of phage to grow on particular bacterial strains.

The sites at which most restriction enzymes cut DNA are quite short, and thus occur not only in phage and bacterial DNA but also, by chance, in the DNA of any organism. These enzymes can therefore be used to isolate unique pieces of DNA from any genome, even the genomes of multicellular organisms containing billions of nucleotides. Once this had been appreciated, many new techniques were rapidly developed: methods of separating the pieces of DNA by gel electrophoresis; techniques for splicing pieces of DNA into carrier 'vector' plasmid or phage DNAs so that this 'recombinant DNA' could be replicated in bacteria and millions of copies made; and the use of DNA hybridisation to identify a particular piece of DNA. Methods for rapidly determining the nucleotide sequence of DNA added the crown to this new technology. The genomes of multicellular organisms were now accessible to direct analysis. This had enormous potential for both basic and medical research.

But the full application of this technology to research was delayed for several years, first by a moratorium called from within the scientific community itself, and subsequently by the need to draw up cumbersome regulations to allay public fears.

"Sometime in 1975, I received a letter from the Secretary of the MRC enjoining me not to do any of these types of experiments because of the moratorium that had been called. This moratorium was actually very easy to obey because I suddenly realised the great merit of something I had discovered very early. Which is the difference between chastity and impotence [see Chapter 2]. We didn't have to be chaste because, not yet having developed this technology ourselves, we were in fact impotent to do anything with it! So of course we could agree to the moratorium immediately. But I could see that in fact this was indeed the kind of work one needed to get into. I immediately recognised that this would be the very way to tackle the genetics of higher organisms and I wanted very much to do it myself. But it became very difficult to actually introduce this programme for the simple reason that it aroused this huge outcry.

This propelled me quite heavily into the more political work of trying to get all of this unlocked. I think that this was the first time that there was an enormous confrontation between, so to speak, science and public interest. And all of these questions that we now live with on a daily basis exploded in a very big way at that time. We lived then in a time where these things had to be handled very carefully."

A meeting was convened in 1975 in Asilomar, California, by the National Academy of Sciences to consider the ethical and legal issues associated with the newly emerging capabilities for gene cloning. The moratorium on recombinant technology was imposed by a majority vote at that meeting until more definitive guidelines could be promulgated.

"I suggested something called the *Book of Man*. At that time of course we still did not know that genes contained introns. So I thought we could easily get all the human genes and glue them on a page of nitrocellulose and this would be the

Book of Man. And you could turn to page forty-eight, line twenty-three, word four, and there you'd have the gene for serum albumin written. So the concept that one could just get the genes by working with DNA was of course very much alive and very exciting. And being in Cambridge, where Fred Sanger was sequencing DNA, we realised that this was on the threshold of the new genetics. And the new genetics was what I became extremely interested in."

Scientists, like the general public, were split about the possible dangers of recombinant DNA technology. Brenner, like most, shared the view that the public uproar, an uproar strongly reinforced by the media, was ridiculous. The power of the media, especially the printed press in the United States, was profound.

"I hadn't appreciated how much things had changed in America. I recalled recently, when Nixon died, that the press had at that time actually succeeded in getting rid of a President of the United States. And organisations like the *Washington Post* were unbelievable in their dreams of omnipotence. At the Asilomar meeting it was agreed that speakers could ask for the [official] recording to be turned off while they said something. The question was then put to the audience – should the press turn off their machines at the same time? We were asked to vote on this, and when they took the vote I was the only one who voted for it. I think there was perhaps one other European who also did. But everybody else voted against it.

At a press conference I was asked by a reporter from the *Washington Post* how dare I come to this country – you know we have freedom of the press and so on – and suggest that the press should be turned off? I said, 'Well look, it was the only time I was given an opportunity of commenting on the presence of the press and I voted this way because I was dead against the press being here!' Well, the man went berserk. He sort of accused me of being a fascist and so on, and he asked, 'Why are you doing this?' And I replied, 'Because I believe in the inalienable right of adult scientists to make fools of themselves in private!' But eventually I came to realise the extent of this change in the American public. The entire atmosphere – which we now take as a given – was that you don't do these sorts of things without these concerns, as the Americans put it, 'reaching' you! And that was something totally different."

With the advent of the Asilomar Conference and its recommendations, national regulatory committees were convened throughout the world, the powers of which were also highly controversial in the scientific community. Guidelines for carrying out recombinant DNA work were initially implemented in the United States, where failure to comply could result in the forfeiture of one's research grant – or even dismissal.

"In America they'd become very anxious about getting licences to do this work. They would settle on anything as long as they got a licence. So an enormous number of categories were invented which were worked out by scientists and which were ludicrous because the dangers, which were strictly conjectural (that is, you *thought* they were dangers), were dependent on where the DNA came from. Now clearly malaria is a dangerous disease. Therefore they said, 'If you clone malaria DNA you have to do this under a very high category,' without taking into consideration what it would actually take to reconstitute malaria from its component DNA molecules. On those grounds, you see, you would have to clone lion DNA at a much higher category than, say, pussy cat DNA because clearly lions are more dangerous than pussy cats! And so this kind of uncanny never-never land which just made no sense became the way in which one did experiments over the next few years.

I spent an inordinate amount of time working in the field and also trying to change things. In the United Kingdom they set up a committee called the Genetic Manipulation Group. It had lots of representatives and we got a workable system going. But one of the things that became perfectly obvious after all of this was established was that no one actually believed it was dangerous! And it's very difficult to get people to play at being safe when they know that something's not dangerous. Everybody knew that if you work with smallpox virus or the AIDS virus you could get it. There *had* been laboratory infections. But to say that DNA cloned from any organism was dangerous was actually beyond scientific belief.

Some of the objections were indeed realistic, especially as they pertained to the safety of what you might call the work force in the laboratory. And in fact we did push regulation in that direction, because this was something tangible that you could actually implement. But what is very difficult to deal with is something that I think comes up with science in general and is impossible to handle – namely the disaster scenarios, the catastrophe scenarios. People like Erwin Chargaff came out and said that we were tampering with evolution and we didn't know what's going to happen. Now, I mean, how on earth can you ask scientists to be responsible for something that might happen ten million years in the future? This is ludicrous! People can't even be responsible for something that will happen next month! But the whole idea that we should admit that we can see that if we do this there is a possibility, however small, as they put it, that in ten million years we humans will be supplanted by cats and therefore we'd better not do this, is just not the way to deal with the world, or with science for that matter!

There were also very complicated issues about the so-called responsibility of scientists, which I've never believed in. I think that what people should do is to act as good social people, as individuals, but it doesn't seem to me reasonable that as a group scientists should have some *special* social responsibility. And of course that comes from the atom bomb. Once you open Pandora's box, so the argument goes, everything gets let loose. Therefore, never let the scientists open Pandora's box. Kill it in the laboratories! Because once it's out, society is incompetent or unable to deal with it.

I once gave a lecture on the irresponsibility of *society*, because that seems to me to be the real issue. The people – as I said in this lecture – polluting the universe aren't the scientists, but everybody's mother, with detergents and so on. And how does everybody's mother get hold of detergents? There are companies that manufacture them. Of course it is a possibility that the chap who first made sodium dodecylsulphate [a detergent], had he had the sense to envisage that in the future ten million people would be putting this in their dishwashers, might have said, 'Well I'd better not publish this and better not let it out. Because I can see that in a hundred years time everything will be wrong!'

The important thing is that science is neutral. If the box can be opened it will be opened. If not now, then later. If not by us, then by other people. And you can't just forbid the search for this or that kind of new knowledge and not for any other, because it's all part of the process. It seems to me that people had better get on with the real question, which is, 'What are you going to do with knowledge once you get it?' And it's not up to us scientists to say that we are to blame, *mea culpa*, we'll stop doing this, we promise that we'll never clone another gene.

Because you would lose a lot from this mentality.

Part of my work became to really try and get the science moving again. One of the things I did was try to create a safe strain of bacteria to work with. I had a very amusing time with this. My argument was that I would 'train' a bacterium to live in heavy water. Once I got it accustomed to live in heavy water it wouldn't be able to live anywhere in the present universe because heavy water was only obtained in pure form in 1935 in Chicago! So I actually grew bacteria for thousands of generations in heavy water. They adapted. And I thought that this would be the absolutely safe strain of *E. coli* because it would only know this kind of particular chemical universe. It would make this sort of work very expensive of course, and it would make organisations like the Norwegian Electricity Company very rich because everybody would have to use heavy water! But alas, I found out that the bacteria could always grow in light water again!

Eventually I did create a safe strain and I had to test it of course. I tested it on myself. Human experimentation was strictly forbidden. But I said that I was testing it on an upper primate. I didn't say it was a human being! In fact I don't count myself as necessarily one! But I showed that my strain was ten million times safer. I wrote two papers – my only papers published by Her Majesty's Stationery Office. They were published as part of an official report.[1] One paper is very interesting because it analysed theoretical pathogenesis. It essentially says, 'Why don't we try to make a real estimate of conjectural dangers and get some numbers? And with these numbers we can begin to compare dangers.' This system is still being used, because once you did this in a quantitative way everything came out very

---

1   Report of the Working Party on the Practice of Genetic Manipulation, 1976 (HMSO, 1978).

simply. You got huge differentials of safety and dangers. And so ultimately, we changed the system here in England, and since that time experimentation in genetic manipulation has been quite acceptable. Of course nothing dangerous has happened in all these years.

Were it not for eventually getting people to think sensibly about this, we could not have had a lot of good work completed so rapidly. Take the AIDS virus for example. The recombinant DNA technology has been invaluable. The AIDS virus was cloned and people could work with the DNA. They could sequence it and they could characterise it very rapidly. If you look at the history of other infectious agents, we accomplished worldwide in one year with the AIDS virus what might have taken twenty years to do with standard methods. So I think that was a very good lesson.

Another remarkable lesson that emerged was, 'Don't worry. If you can think of something dangerous, nature's probably done it!' So I decided to think of something that's dangerous and then see how one would deal with this. I surmised about taking the cholera toxin gene and putting it in a vector in the bacterium *E. coli* so that the vector could infect other bacteria. I considered that to be a dangerous experiment. Well, in fact it's been done – by nature! The gene for the same kind of toxin, called shiga toxin, exists in a bacteriophage related to the common bacteriophages that we use in our laboratories. This phage infects the *Shigella* bacterium, which is quite closely related to the common *E. coli*. That's how nature has done it. Of course she always has priority over us!

As I say, I spent an inordinate amount of my time on this. But I think it was basically required, in the sense that if people who were sensible had not participated in this process we would have been left with some of the difficulties that they have in Germany today, or in parts of Japan, where it's impossible to do genetic experimentation.

I wrote an article for a journal in the mid-1980s and I said that in the history of biological science we can think of two epochs – BC, which stands for 'before cloning', and AD, which stands for 'after DNA'. Before this junction, which dates back to about 1975, everything seemed hopeless. We thought we'd never get down to the molecular biology of the genes with *C. elegans*. But now it's rather banal. It's commonplace. Anybody can do it. Anyone can clone a gene; they can sequence it, they can ask 'Does this look like something I've seen before,' and 'How can I fit this into the broader picture of biology?' So this has opened up large areas of biology to everyone. And there's no doubt about it; this explosion turned developmental biology into a real science."

This contribution to the sociology of science completed, in the late 1970s Brenner undertook what he describes as a big mistake in his life – he became the Director of the MRC Laboratory of Molecular Biology.

"I did that out of some kind of loyalty to the institution. I became the Director-elect some two years before, because the MRC Laboratory now had tremendous financial difficulties. It was no longer properly funded. I mean it was ludicrous to work in a laboratory where you ran out of methanol. There wasn't any money to buy methanol! So I took over the budget in 1977 when I was made the Director-elect, and became the Director in 1979.

As I look back on it I think that was a big mistake, because it's not the sort of thing I like doing. I soon realised that people who go into these sorts of positions become windows. That is, the people above them look through them at the people below. You become a mediator between two impossible groups – the monsters above and the idiots below. Also, in these sorts of jobs you run out of imagination very quickly. One can argue that, in science, people can be divided into three classes depending on how much in the future they have to worry about! The active scientist is only worried about two or three days into the future. A few senior people are worried about the next month. But directors of laboratories have to worry about years into the future.

One also had to worry about renewal. I had great concern for how one keeps a great laboratory going for the future. And the future, I always felt, is strongly assured by getting new blood and having rapid turnover. I adopted a policy of hiring new people, but my colleagues didn't agree with this. So after a while we didn't see eye to eye on this. I ignored them for a while because I firmly believed that bringing in new subjects and new people was the essence, the core of science. I spent quite a lot of time fiddling around with budgets and keeping the books and looking after the till. But I decided that I had just had enough of this. I had become interested in the nervous system again and I wanted to get back to science.

The MRC had appointed me until age sixty. But at age fifty-eight they asked me 'Do you wish to continue as Director?' and I emphatically said 'No. I do not wish to continue as Director! I want to get out! I want to get back to science.' I managed to get out a year later, in 1986, and I started another unit, to work on the new genetics. The 'new' genetics can be distinguished from the 'old' genetics because now we could go from the genes outward, whereas in the 'old' genetics we went from the phenotype inwards, to look for genes."

Brenner's interest now turned to the human genome and the Human Genome Project, a visionary project to map all the genes in the human genome and, eventually, to sequence it.

"I had made contact with the people who were interested in starting the Human Genome Programme. Bob Sinsheimer had his first meeting on this in 1984. I couldn't go to that meeting but I sent two people from the Laboratory. But they had a repeat meeting in 1985 in Santa Fe, New Mexico and I went to that. I believed that this programme was going to be the new way of doing biological science, and that it would open up enormous vistas to us. So the Human Genome Project, as it was called, became a central interest of mine.

I had long been interested in genomic studies in the sense that I realised that once you could clone DNA you could map it in some way. And I spent, it's now nearly twenty years, trying to work out a simple way of doing this so that someone could make a genetic map of a higher organism, on the kitchen table basically. I'm not there yet, I'm nearly there. We started doing work on bacteria to try and map their genes. That got quite far. John Sulston joined me in this bacterial mapping and then he decided he would try and apply the technology to *C. elegans*. So the *C. elegans* project then grew into an enormous genome project, which now has the dedicated aim of sequencing the entire worm genome.

I decided that I would go for the *human* genome. The reason for that is that I believe that if we're going to do this amount of work on an animal, one animal, let's choose the animal that's of most interest. And from this egocentric point of view I think man is extremely interesting. The point is that you were now no longer conditioned by experimental constraints. When we did classical experimental genetics we had to go through endless selections to get an organism that fitted into the window of the electron microscope, and that would grow rapidly in a laboratory, and that you could freeze, and had the appropriate life cycle, and that you could do experiments with. This placed enormous constraints on what you could choose. Half of the art of choosing was, in fact, a piece of science in its own right.

When I started with *C. elegans* in 1963 I was almost forty. Many of my colleagues were thinking of retiring into administration and that sort of thing. But I continued working with it extensively and personally for another ten years. I then decided to give it up. There were lots of people doing this sort of thing then, and they were far more competent at doing what needed to be done than I was! We did continue with this until the early 1980s, but basically my mind was going somewhere else.

You know, the English crystallographer Desmond Bernal once compared science to a chess game. He said, 'There's the opening game, there's the middle game, and there's the end game.' Now, of course very few people get a chance to play the end game. Most people are in the middle game. But I find the most wonderful thing in science is the opening game, when there's nothing else there. That's when I think you can exercise a tremendous amount of freedom of intellectual choice. Bernal himself was extremely good at the opening game. I think that's the challenge. And so having played the opening game with *C. elegans*, it was now in the middle game where there were lots of people taking pawns and moving knights around the board. So I thought I'd better go and find somewhere else to play another game.

You might think that the age of nearly sixty is probably not a good time to start something new in science, but in fact it is. I like to think that people who get to be age sixty already know too much about the subjects they've worked in to be of any use anyway. Because, as I said before, I've always been a strong believer in the value of ignorance. I think that when you know too much you're dangerous in a subject because you can deter originality in others. So the big thing is to get out of it and go and look for something else to do.

Also, once you get to the age of sixty you begin to forget things and your knowledge is decaying all the time. That's quite useful actually! But it's also quite dangerous because you find yourself doing things that you did fifteen years ago and forgot about and actually go through again and rediscover. That's why I think people should change their subjects very frequently. I think that the best scientists do that.

Well, now we could effectively clone genes and sequence them. Therefore we didn't have to do mutant hunts any more. We could actually find the wild-type genes – they were there. Then we could ask, 'What happens if I make a defect in this gene?' It's been called 'reverse genetics', but it's not really reverse genetics, it's 'inside-out genetics'. The whole history of biology is characterised by pursuing functions from the outside, from the phenotype. You find people who suffer at high altitude and you discover that they have abnormal red blood cells and then you show that they have a protein that has an abnormal way of aggregating, and finally you show that there's a protein with one amino acid change and that's the sickle-cell mutation. That took decades to do.

Now we can start at the other end, which is to find the wild-type gene. Since we know the genetic code, we can just write down the protein. And as information collects about proteins and what they do, we may be able to map this in terms of phenotypic function. So here's a new approach to genetics. It liberates us from the life cycles of organisms. We had been bound to always do genetic crosses. Our experiments depended on taking genotypes apart, seeing what happens, and putting them together again and seeing what happens. And when we looked for experimental organisms they had to have easy life cycles. They had to have rapid ones, so that we could do a lot of experiments and didn't have to wait a year or two years for the answer – in that case we might well have forgotten what the question was by the time we got the answer. I remember giving my first lecture on this in about 1986, in which I said, 'We have been liberated from the tyranny of the life cycles of organisms, from their modes of reproduction. We can do genetics now on everything, anything. Giant redwoods, grapes and, most importantly, human beings.'

Now of course there were lots of organisms that it would be interesting to know about, but which were intractable, or in some cases illegal, to do genetic experiments with. That's why the genetics of man had gone so slowly. We could only rely on certain genetic markers and so on. But being able to approach that from the DNA seemed to me to unify the whole of biology at one blow. And when it was first suggested we should sequence the whole of the human genome, just like the genomes of smaller organisms have been sequenced, I thought that was a great idea. But to jump from 50,000 bases to 3 billion – that's a 10^6 jump. That was an act – I wouldn't call it of imagination – but certainly of daring. But a lot of people got together to say, 'Yes, this is something that we would want to do.'

There was gigantic antagonism of scientists to this project. It was pictured that there'd be a giant factory somewhere that would generate DNA sequences. Such factories are viable enough, but not in the context of science. Even nowadays I have to convince scientists that there are people in the world who want to do this sort of work, it's a job. They wouldn't be interested in the results. Because what they'd be interested in is the money, so that on Friday afternoon they can take that money and then go and pursue their interests, like having boats or gardens and so on.

Scientists don't imagine that there are people like this. They think that everybody is a student with a kind of inalienable right to be a genius and that this sort of work will actually clamp them. But it's not true. There are lots of people happy at this type of work. In fact, I thought we could actually do this by having something that was like a bingo hall. We could have these machines and put up the sequence of the day. People would actually pay to come and operate these machines and we'd have a prize. It would cost you £10 to operate the machine. But if you happened to get the sequence of the day there'd be a prize of a £1000. I thought we'd be deluged with people wanting to come and play these machines, and we could put them up in shopping malls and supermarkets. We'd get the sequence done very easily. Indeed, although there are 3 billion base pairs, you realise in principle it could be done in an afternoon, let us say, by the population of China. Of course there's a bit of a problem organising the population to do it!

A lot of scientists complained that this is going to bring in 'big science' and everybody will be enslaved in some way. And then of course the *real* motives surfaced: it would divert money from them! So the real issue about whether the genome project should be funded or not was that it had to satisfy some kind of threshold of new money so that it wouldn't be taking it away from the scientists. Otherwise there would be screams and shouts. And that's really what all the politics was about. Where can we get new money?

I had by this time, by 1986, officially left the Laboratory of Molecular Biology, although I was still physically housed in it; I had a unit of my own and I decided I would do human genome work with my own money. I'd just been given a Jeantet Award, which had a research fund of about £300,000 that I could use any way I liked. So I started to hire people and we began to pursue our approach to it. Our approach was not to attempt to sequence the human genome, but to do it in the old way of looking for genes. The best way to look for genes was of course to look for their complementary copies, cDNAs. The idea was to characterise cDNAs and put them on a map. It seemed to me to be such a straightforward thing so I said right at the beginning, 'Let's construct a gene map.' Because that's what geneticists do. But of course there were enormous discussions as to whether this was going to be a physical map or a genetic map, or this kind of map, or the other. There's really only one map that you need, which is where the genes are. Give us the genes and tell us where they are! That was the task.

I spent a lot of time trying to negotiate a special programme in the United Kingdom, which I managed to do. And in fact did something which I think is totally remarkable for the 1980s, which was actually to generate new money for medical research, because throughout this period the government had been whittling away at the funds for research. And we actually created *new* money. The greatest benefit that brought is that if you go to laboratories today you will see numbers of young people, students and post-docs, that this brought into the field. Human genome research, rather than being a kind of 'big science' factory, has turned out to have attracted the most interesting, and I think the brightest, of the scientists. I think they recognise that this is fundamental biology of the highest form. I think the Americans did make it banal – that's the only word that I can use – by commercialising it. But the project still remains.

I had come to the conclusion a long time ago that the human genome was full of rubbish [see Chapter 8], and I propagated this widely. Carefully making the distinction between two kinds of rubbish: namely 'junk', which is rubbish that is kept, and 'garbage', which is rubbish that is thrown out. It turns out that most languages use two words to specify this distinction. In Japanese, *gomi* is rubbish you throw out, garbage, while *garakuta* is junk that you keep. And of course if there is rubbish in your genome it must be junk because if it were garbage it wouldn't be there. So I asked the question, 'Is there a vertebrate somewhere that may not have acquired all this junk?'

At Woods Hole in the late 1960s, I taught courses in which it worried me that there seemed to be organisms that had too much DNA, and as part of this interest I read in the fantastic library of the Woods Hole Marine Biology Laboratory. I was familiar with a journal called *The American Naturalist* because I'd been a reader of it for many years. (It's a journal which I should say is *not* a nudist magazine!) In one issue I found a paper by a man named Heingardner. Heingardner had measured the DNA content of many species of fish and had shown that there were some that had DNA contents about an eighth that of man; eight times smaller genomes. Now at the time if you asked anybody 'What do you think about this fish with eight times less DNA than man?', the answer was, 'Clearly that's all the DNA the fish deserve! You know, I reckon I'm eight times more complicated than this fish!' We had no idea of what all this DNA content meant then, especially since we were only at the beginnings of discovering repetitive DNA and so on. A second paper was published in 1983 which showed that there is, in fact, very little repetitive DNA in these fish genomes. It's about ninety percent unique. So I thought this fish genome may be interesting to look at.

I tried to get these fish for quite some time. They were puffer fish. But I decided that such is the unreliability of natural sources that we would no sooner start to work on this but we would find that some pollution, or some fire, or something else had got rid of them in the world – they'd become extinct. So I decided that I would get the one specimen of this fish which is actually cultivated for food in Japan. And this is the fugu, the Japanese puffer fish. So I went to Japan to try to organise this. When people asked me 'Why are you interested in this?' I replied, 'Let me give you a little talk on junk!'

Nobody believed this stuff. They said the measurements must be wrong. It can't be that you have something with so little DNA. Well, to cut a long story short, I managed to find a group of young people to work with me on this. The first thing we wanted to show is that this fish has the same number of genes as we do. Because if it had only one-eighth the number of genes then it wasn't very interesting. And we were able to do that by what, I think, is a very pretty experiment. What we did is to use a new technique called statistical genomics. We just took 600 pieces of [fugu] DNA randomly and sequenced them and asked, 'How many genes can we find that have already been found in other vertebrates, and in particular in mammals?' We could then calculate the probability of finding these genes in these genomes. And what we found is that it was eight times more enriched in fugu. So we proved that fugu and people had more or less the same number of genes. But the fugu genome is much more compact.

I like to call the fugu genome the 'discount genome', because you get a 90% discount on sequencing. I'd now enhanced the sequencing job about ten-fold. I'd fulfilled the great technical requirement which everybody said we should strive for – a ten-fold gain in technology every five years. And I'd done that in a few months just by choosing the right organism! We now have a lot of people coming to our lab to find pieces of fish DNA that correspond to this and that, and I'm encouraging as many people as possible to work on this.

Let us assume that certain groups of genes have stayed together throughout this whole period of about half a billion years of evolution from fish to man. Many people can map a human gene – let's say a gene for breast cancer – but they can only narrow it to somewhere in a piece of DNA that's about a million base pairs. Now to sequence through a million base pairs and find the gene is enormously tedious and time consuming. What *we* are saying is that you'll only have to sequence 100,000 or 125,000 base pairs. Because what you do is get the right piece of the fugu genome and then move along. And whereas on the average a gene in man is about 50,000 bases long, a gene in fugu is about 6,000 bases.

We have found that all the intervening sequences [introns] are present in the fugu genome. They're in the same place, so these are the same genes. But they are very tiny and also the genes are close together. They're not separated by large amounts of junk DNA. We have sequenced many fugu genes and compared them with human genes, and in all cases we find the same number of introns. But the introns are tiny in the fish whereas they can be enormous in the human or mammalian genome. So this enables you to find human genes simply by using fish. It also enables you to characterise human genes, which are enormous. For example, the gene that's affected in the disease Duchenne muscular dystrophy, called dystrophin, is 2.8 megabases long. That's nearly three million base pairs. Whereas the part that we have already sequenced in the fish has been reduced by a factor of twenty in size. So if the whole thing were to follow properly, the fish gene would be of the order of about 150,000 base pairs. Which means that we could characterise the gene very quickly.

I don't want to set up a big institute to do this. I think it should be dispersed. I would like to follow what I call the 'Talleyrand principle', which is to never do for yourself that which you can get other people to do for you! I think that what we will find immediately is how these pieces of DNA in this fish correspond to pieces in the human genome. So we will see how a primordial vertebrate genome got fragmented in different ways as we evolved from fish. Not only that, we can also find out what happened in evolution. Or at least we can make a good approximation to it.

Let us suppose that I were to start a new genetic programme and I wrote a grant saying, 'I want to get a fish in the lab and I want to make mutants and I want to turn it into a man.' Because that's the really interesting thing: how fish became men in the course of time. And you're sort of a little fish at some point of your own development, you know! You've got little gills and so on. We could at least try to explain how you went from being a little fish to being a little man! If I did this no one would give me an absolute penny of course. But you see, it's already been done for us. We've got the human mutants and we still have some representatives of the original stock, the fish. So why don't I just do the following. I'll take a gene out of the fish and put it into a man. You can't do that, right, so I'll do it in a mouse. And now I'll ask for that gene, 'Do you work in the mouse?' Now the mouse could be argued, from the point of view of physiology and anatomy, to have a 'fishy' part, and also to have something that got added on later in evolution. But there still is a 'fishy' part to the mouse. The immunology will still be 'fishy'. The lungs certainly won't be, because they aren't present in fish. So if I find a gene that expresses in the lungs of a mouse and I find the same gene in a fish, I can ask whether that fish gene will express in the lungs of a mouse. If it doesn't, I have to say that gene simply retained information and therefore I should look at the mouse gene to see what happened during evolution. Have other parts been added on? Has it moved to another place perhaps, where it has different regulation? That's probably what would have happened.

But in the other case, if the fish gene expresses in the mouse – that is, you can't tell the difference between a mouse without the gene and one with the fish gene – then I would have the right to say that evolution went to a higher level in the programme but this gene remained the same. So what we can then identify is those invariant parts of the genome that stayed the same. To put it another way: if we make two animals that are absolutely identical except that one has this piece of DNA from the mouse and the other has the analogous piece from a fish, I argue that if you cannot tell the difference between them, then anything that's common in their sequence is that which works. And of course you want to go far away [in evolutionary distance], like fish and mouse, because you want time to have corroded everything that is non-essential. If you compare things like mice to man there hasn't been enough evolutionary time. We contain 'mousy' features simply because we came from something that also gave rise to mouse. But fish is so far away that, effectively, we've put enough noise into the rubbish to be able to say 'This is the rubbish; this is junk.' So I think that is a rigorous experimental approach to these problems, and I believe that we will be doing the genetics of evolution in the next few years.

I think this is really the way to do the genetics of complex regulation. I have called this 'genetics by composition' rather than 'genetics by decomposition'. I think that this is going to be the way in which we can tackle all the complex problems. What is beautiful is that we will be able to provide evolutionary explanations of what there is in the genome now. And since the whole of living matter is accessible to this, we can ask questions in a deeply analytical way about problems that you couldn't even begin to frame before, by just using this technology. In essence, a transgenic animal or a transgenic cell is just a cross of a genome with a gene!"

10
Endnotes

… on reading

"One day Francis Crick put a rather large sign in the office which said, 'Reading rots the mind.' I think he saw it somewhere and had it enlarged and pinned it up. I don't know what it was intended for really. It was perhaps in some ways a facetious comment related to Rutherford's famous remark to the effect that, 'There are two kinds of science: there is stamp collecting and there is physics.' To which I once replied 'Well it turns out there are some stamps worth collecting!'

But the point is that biology is a subject in which you have to read extensively. Everything is so specific. Animals differ from each other, they differ from plants, from bacteria. The diversity of life and the diversity of investigation into this is enormous. And you have to know a lot, especially if you were going to do

experimental work. Because as I've said extensively, I've always felt that somewhere there's the ideal organism to do the work with, and if you can find this in
the literature it can cut years of work for you.

Francis himself read a lot. So I don't really know why he put that sign up. I think
that what he wanted to say is that science is not just a scholarly enterprise, embedded as it were, in an ancient university where people just compile compendia. In
other words, reading is not enough. You have to think as well. I agree with him.
Reading's *not* enough. But sometimes *thinking* isn't enough either, because in the
end it's *doing* what counts and so *doing* is what our business is about.

I read all the time. If there was anything on a piece of paper I read it. It's the one
thing I like to do. I like to go to libraries and browse. I spend a lot of time doing
this. At the Scripps Research Foundation in La Jolla, California I spent two hours
every day just going to the library and looking at the journals, just seeing what's
there, reading a bit of this or that. Even the *Journal of Bone and Joint Surgery.*

I had an incredible reprint collection. And so did Francis actually. In fact, we put
ours together and I've still got it. These reprints go back to – at least in my case –
the mid 1940s, and in Francis' case, later. They're arranged alphabetically so you
have to know the author to retrieve anything. Reprints are wonderful because
you had to write for all of these and so they show me what I've actually read. In
fact I noticed that in Judson's history he referred to a paper by Kurt Stern that contained an early speculation on coding. I actually drew his attention to that because
I had a reprint of this paper which I had acquired because I was an avid reader of
the *Yale Journal of Biology and Medicine*, which of course nobody's ever heard of
today. I found this article and I wrote to Kurt Stern from South Africa, and I got

a reprint. This is a style that I got accustomed to in South Africa because that's the only way you could get hold of interesting things to read there.

So reading is important. But as I said before I think that knowledge can be dangerous to research. A modicum of ignorance is absolutely essential. Because otherwise you don't try anything new. And that's why in any line of research people can get saturated very quickly – because they just know everything. When a student comes to you and says 'Why don't we try this?' You tend to say 'Oh, don't be silly, you know, that'll never work.'

I think that these days finding a book that can effectively introduce you to a subject is quite difficult. Most people today only learn by going to courses. They have to have a course of instruction; they have to have a lecture; they have to go to a summer course. The whole idea of learning by yourself is absent now. When I wanted to learn about a new subject, like computation, I found that I had to read the book until it was right for me. The author thought he had the correct way of teaching me the subject. But I found that I had to start at Chapter 7 and then read the first half of Chapter 1 and then to Chapter 10, and so on. In that way I was able to create my own path through this new subject. I think that is very important.

Francis read a lot. He read all of Hubel and Wiesel's papers. He found it very difficult. He also read a lot of the anatomy of the brain. And in fact, for the last thirty years Francis has done very little except read in order to acquire the background to deal with such an immense problem as the functions of the brain. So perhaps his mind is now rotten!

I'm interested in reading philosophy; that's an old interest. As I've grown older I have become tremendously interested in biography, history, and in particular autobiography, because I've come to the conclusion that the past does live on in individuals and it's very interesting to be able to read about it. One of my hobbies is to collect the writing of scientists about themselves and about other people. I'm very interested in writings that create a social environment, whether they're fiction or factual. One of the greatest things I've read is the first volume of Richard Goldschmidt's life. The second volume is boring because it's all about his travels in Japan. But the first volume is amazing because it recreates what it was like to be a student in Germany in the 1890s, at the peak of German culture, with the kind of biologists there were then, and how important the museums were in teaching biology. And how really brilliant biologists could never get a Chair but became curators of museums and taught schoolboys biology. Those books seem to me to bring back lost worlds and I think they have tremendous value.

The other book that I think everybody should read is the one that Max Born wrote about his own life, for his family, with its descriptions of pre-war Germany and what it was like to be Jewish, and visiting this certain place only on a certain day each year. Born was very puzzled that as a young man he had to go on this long hike on a certain day each year, and he noticed that all the other people who went on this hike were Jewish. And that was because Cosima Wagner, Richard Wagner's wife, held an open day at her estate for Jews once a year. Because she wouldn't invite them any other time [Richard Wagner was a notorious anti-Semite]."

… on losing one's memory

"I used to remember more than I do now. But that's because I think my memory stores are just full. I don't think my memory's failing me, I've just reached saturation. In fact, I take this very seriously because some years ago when I was a member of an MRC committee, there were certain papers I refused to read, and when people asked me, 'Have you read the papers?' I said 'No.' And when they said, 'Why not?' I said, 'I now divide papers into three classes: those that give me information, those that have no effect, and those that remove information from my head. And the latter is in this class and I'm not going to give over to rubbish like this.'

Ironically I can actually remember when my memory did first began to fail me. Miranda Robertson [from the journal *Nature*] asked me who invented interferon, and I couldn't remember. But the interesting thing is that after a while I said, 'It was Abraham.' But Abraham didn't invent interferon, he invented cephalosporin. The person who invented interferon is Isaacs. Now you will immediately note the connection from enforced study of the Old Testament when I was young. Which shows you something about how memory is stored.

I make a lot of notes. I make extensive notes on everything. I travel around and write down things. I used to write things on index cards in the old days. I now tend to write them in note books – exercise books we used to call them in South Africa. I have a lot of exercise books which have references to this, that and the other. Some have actually developed into whole lines of research. Leo Szilard was like that. Szilard always wrote things in exercise books. But what was remarkable was that he threw them away as soon as he finished them. I can remember being in the Pasteur Institute one time when Leo was talking to Mel Cohen. Mel was telling Leo about his new theories on antibody formation, which Leo wrote down. When he came to the end of an exercise book he threw it in the garbage can and took another one out of his pocket and went on writing!

But of course in these days where the literature is so enormous one just can't do that anymore. I used to actually read *Chemical Abstracts* regularly. And I'd keep notes. This was before the days of copying machines, of course. So effectively you had to follow the literature this way."

... on personal strengths and weaknesses

"I think my real skills are in getting things started – that's gone through my whole life. In fact, it's what I enjoy most, the opening game. And I'm afraid that once it gets past that point I get rather bored and want to do other things. So being a permanent post-doc is really very attractive to me, and is I think the exciting part of intellectual life in science.

The other thing I'm rather good at is talking. When Fred Sanger was asked to give me a recommendation I was told that he said, 'Oh, Brenner, the man who talks a lot!' So I believe that keeping up the conversation is one of the important roles one can have in science. The whole idea that science is conducted by people working alone in rooms and struggling with the forces of nature is absolutely ridiculous. It is a social activity of the highest sort. And so keeping up the conversation, doing experiments with words, is very important. I'm fascinated by that, and I think that's how ideas can emerge. Most of what I say is rubbish, but amidst the kind of stream of unconsciousness, if I can coin a phrase, there is the odd idea that can be developed into something.

I'm also rather good at brainwashing, which is to persuade people to do things that their upbringing tells them they ought not to be doing. I'm not a very good administrator. In fact I'm rather hopeless. I get by with improvisation, which I suppose is the way we should do it. And as I've got older I look less and less ahead. If you're only worried about what's going to happen next month, it makes it easier than to worry what's going to happen over the next five years.

One of my weaknesses, and it's something I've always regretted, is that I'm not as good a mathematician as I really wanted to be. I find mathematics very difficult. In fact it is computers that gave me a great hitch up in the world, because I turned out to be quite a good programmer, and I can understand all of that. But trying to do mathematics – which is something I really wanted to do and thought that I should be able to do well – I find difficult, and I'm not very good at.

I'm also not very good at getting things right the first time around. But I think that's a strength and not a weakness, because I think if one gets it straight the first time around it's probably boring. And getting it wrong half the time is the interesting thing.

I'm very bad at writing. I really resent writing and in fact had Francis not locked me up in a room during our career together I probably wouldn't have written as many papers as I did. Because somehow once it's solved and I know the answer, all the rest of that – which is writing it up for publication and dealing with referees and editors – just seems so much of an unnecessary boring appendage to the actual work of scientific creation, that I would have been quite happy if I'd had a ghost in the lab who would have written my papers for me. I'm not very good at that.

Other people have told me what my weaknesses are, but I don't agree with them. Like I'm insulting, I'm arrogant and so on. I don't think I *am* actually. I think I'm pretty honest basically, and I think I know what I'm trying to do. I think that science is so important, and what we're trying to do is so important within it, that I sometimes *do* express impatience with the sort of people who lie in the way.

One of my great advantages is I have a good sense of humour, particularly about myself. And that's one of the great things that I think one ought to have. I think one should always have a complete sense of how ludicrous one can be; I think that's very important. Pomposity is one of my great fears. I think pomposity in an old man is terrible. Of course pomposity in a young man is absolutely beyond the pale!

After that, I consider that I've been very lucky to have survived this whole path in science and have been able to indulge in what I wanted to do. I've always said that if one can do what one is interested in and be of benefit to mankind, why not?"

... on creativity

"This is a subject that preoccupies a lot of people because everybody would like to be creative, and everybody wants to know where they can they get it from. Of course if you could get a packet of creativity and buy it somewhere, that would be the ideal thing. One of the things about creativity is not to be afraid of saying the wrong thing. I think that's terribly important. Too many people are brought up, especially in our culture, to think that everything should be rational, should be worked out, and that daring ideas shouldn't be uttered, simply because they are most likely to be wrong the first time around. Another thing that is terribly important to creativity is day-dreaming.

But the essence of science is to realise it, to implement it. And one of the things about creativity is to absolutely know where and how one can prove something. I know there's a lot spoken about the philosopher Karl Popper's approach to this, in which one should work out ways of disproving one's own theories. But I don't think that Popper was too cognizant of the psychology of scientists. He may know something about the philosophy of science, but you find me a scientist who's actually going to sit down and work out a way of disproving his results! Because most of us, realising the pernicketiness of nature and the unreliability of nature, have to work hard to prove our results. The first time an experiment is done it's likely not to work. Not because the theory is wrong, but just because the whole entropic universe is reaching us as soon as we start to dabble in it. So it takes a lot of creativity to actually do something which is a bit irrational – a feeling that this is the right thing, and that one will go to some lengths to realise it.

I'm doing something now which is quite interesting, because it has involved turning things upside down. And I think that turning things upside down is something that we are not encouraged to do by our culture. Our culture has imposed upon us that we should start at point A and proceed by logical steps to B, C and D. But it sometimes is useful to ask whether in fact the effect is actually the cause, if I can put it that way. I think inversion is sometimes a very useful way of being able to see things from another point of view. What people should realise is that it takes some kind of iron censor within oneself not to fall too much in love with one's own theories. They should be treated as mistresses to be discarded once the pleasure is over! I think that's a very important thing, and it's one of the characteristics of science that you must be ruthless towards your loved ones. When your theories go ugly, kill them. Get rid of them. I once invented a phrase called Occam's broom, or Occam's brush, as we say, to sweep under the carpet what you must in order to leave your hypotheses consistent. But one cannot go on sweeping things under the carpet, especially once the carpet has got to an altitude of about ten feet!

I've always felt that science makes completely contradictory demands on the people who work in it. It asks you to be highly imaginative, yet it asks you to put on blinders and drive through brick walls if necessary to get the answer. It asks you to be passionate about invention, but it also asks you to be ruthless and cut off your own hand if it comes to that. There are very few people who can contribute these opposites. Looking at my students, I've often found that all the characteristics of the one half were in one student, and all the characteristics of the other half were in another student. There are brilliant people who can never accomplish anything. And there are people that have no ideas, but can do things. And if only one could chimerise them – join them into one person – one would have a good scientist. Perhaps that's why science has to operate as a group, as a social unit.

The way I do my thinking is to bounce lots of balls in my head at the same time. Bounce, bounce, bounce. And if you go on bouncing you begin to notice that sometimes two balls are bouncing together. Those, I think, are the connections we have to make, and that means that you've just got to go on thinking about things and asking, 'If it were like this, what would be the outcome?' That's a very important thing to do in biology.

… on personal achievements

"I've had many different kinds of achievement. I think C. *elegans* is a monumental achievement because it generated a kind of industry of science. But if I think about intellectual achievement then it would be in the classical genetics of the *rII* gene of bacteriophage. And the two things here are the triplet nature of the genetic code and the decoding of suppression triplets. That, I would say, had some intellectual content and – if I were to use words like 'brilliant' – was brilliant, in the sense that it shone.

I think that the messenger RNA experiment is something that will be remembered for the simple reason that historically it came at an important time and bridged something that, at least in the minds of most people, was proving to be a complete block to further advancement. Of course what drove it came from many sources, and my contribution was just one little thing. I think my great contribution was to find a way of doing a decisive experiment. When I look back on the messenger RNA experiment some of the things we in our Popperian enthusiasm wished to disprove appear so ludicrous now. People wonder why one wanted to disprove that proteins were made on DNA. I mean, surely this was such a ridiculous thing to have to do. But we didn't know what was going on and so eliminating those possibilities was very important then. Yes, I think that messenger RNA will be the thing!

I've always felt much more confident in myself when I'm outside the mainstream. I've been a rebel, or as I was once called, an *enfant terrible*. Although being close to the age of seventy it's pretty hard to maintain that position. But being a rebel has always appealed to me, largely because I'm convinced that the standard parts of any activity are already petrified at the core. And therefore being a rebel is a cheap way of getting out of being conventional. Unsuccessful rebels never live to be known, of course, and the successful rebels are condemned to be the conventional people of the future! As I once said, 'It's remarkable how quickly young Turks turn into old Greeks.' To try and escape from that has certainly been one of my great ambitions. And perhaps that's why I now am changing my field more frequently. I calculate that if I go on at this rate and live long enough I'll be in a new field every week!"

… on competition and fraud in science

"One thing that is very important to say about this topic is that if you're always doing new things there's very little competition. It could be argued that in my career I got out when the competition got hot, if you like. Or maybe I got out when the science got cool; that's another way of putting it. I don't think one should be affected by competition, although I think a lot of people are. I've always said that if my lab started to be driven by the forces of competition, as many labs are, then we were in for a bad time. For the simple reason that a whole lot of very different things begin to operate, which can lead to ruin. It must be our work which has the greatest meaning for us. And so I've always believed that the people working with me should feel that they're out there alone, and that they can give the problems their total attention and not worry that there are twenty-five hundred people sitting in Paducah Tech who are going to scoop them.

And I have to say that's a great morale builder in a lab, and that's what I think one wants one's young people to feel. Because the rest of their lives are going to be spent in dealing with these social forces. When other people start to work with what you're doing it's okay, because I think we've encouraged them in some way and because they in fact help to build up our reputation. As I said before, I'm a great follower and admirer of Prince Talleyrand. Talleyrand was a remarkable person, a survivor. He was Napoleon's foreign minister and he persisted throughout the most incredible changes of the regimes in France and survived to come out at the other end. He had one remark which I have always thought is important. That is never do for yourself that which you can get other people to do for you. We don't want to eat the world, but if we can get other people to help digest it, that becomes a very important part of science.

About fraud, I remember a meeting in which someone stood up and said, 'Let's get crime off the streets and back into the labs where it belongs!' I think fraud in science is a product of two things, actually. First, it's a product of the work structure, because we now have a managerial structure in many labs where there are generals and captains and corporals. There's a whole hierarchy of people who work in the lab. And in general the head of a lab has no direct connection with the bench. Now, that is bad. Because somebody may make an honest mistake – I know things like this have happened – and come to you and say, 'I've found this!' Usually the supervisor sends him back to repeat it, or preferably do it in another way to support it.

But sometimes it may strike home in the lab chief's mind that this may be a very novel finding. And so he immediately says, 'That means such and such and such and such. Now, if you go and do the following experiment and you get the following answer, then it could mean this and that.' And indeed the person goes and does the experiment, and doesn't get *quite* the answer. It may need a little bit of massaging. That's not fraud; that is what I call embezzlement. Everybody believes that effectively one day it'll come right and everything will be put back and no one will know. So that's the embezzler, who takes £10 out of the till every Friday night and lays it on the horses. What he thinks is that one day his horse will win and he'll put all the money back and no one will know. I think a lot of that goes on. If you're doing experiments yourself, and you learn what all the snags are, and you know that you're working as part of a group, then it's very hard to get that kind of co-operative crime.

The other things that are being driven now are the material aspects of science: getting enough money for the lab. I think that quite a lot of activities there can lead to, if not fraud, certainly exaggeration, if one can put it this way. There's a lot of concealment nowadays. A lot of work is kept secret and there's no free exchange in the sense that people don't tell you what they're doing if they think you'll get there first. So competition does make for a kind of struggle that has its bad effects.

If you ask young people today what the rewards are of being a scientist, you'll find that many people think the rewards are to win a lot of prizes and get a lot of money. Perhaps have a piece of a company, and get promoted, and have grants, and have a big group and have all the material things. Some people want to have publications and have them in the proper journals. People fight and scream in order to get their publications into the journals that have somehow become fashionable. But really, the great thing about science is that you can actually solve a problem. You can take something which is confused, a mess, and not only find a solution, but prove it's the right one. That to me is really what should drive us. And these other things ought to be dismissed. Maybe we ought to just put the word 'commercial' in front of all the other things: the *Journal of Commercial Molecular Biology*, or the *Journal of Commercial Neurobiology*, and let people publish there. That's exactly what I think is the bad face of biology.

There is the problem of the scientist who gets hold of an idea that he then falls in love with and can't let go. Often because the idea is so far out that he's certain that no one else has thought of it, and he really wants to bring this new torch of knowledge to mankind. And, of course, achieve fame and wealth at the same time! Many people do this starting with a mistake. I'm not suggesting that they invent observations. But the observations are wrong. They're due to dirty tubes or running their fingers across a petri dish, or leaving a window open, which can cause the most surprising things to grow on your petri dishes! They start with a fluctuation of the world – generated by Murphy's law basically – and they come to believe it, and start doing experiments which, although they should at some point lead them to question the observation, nevertheless drive them on.

In fact one of the most famous things of this sort was in a subject that I gave the name of 'hydroimmunology'. This man Benveniste believed that he had some immune phenomenon which he could observe after infinite dilution. So he suggested that antibody molecules had left their memory in the structure of the water molecules. Now, that's a great theory! But the other possibility was that these experiments were simply wrong – which they almost certainly were! When I was asked about this, and I was told that he had made dilutions below the value of Avogadro's number I asked, 'Had he tried avocado's number?' And when people said, 'What is that?' I told them, 'It's the number of molecules in a guacamole.' I actually managed to get that story published in Science – without referees!"

... on scientific heroes

"There are many people whom I admire, both people I've known and whom I've read about. von Neumann is a great scientific hero to me, because he seemed to have something special. Of course it may be envy rather than admiration, but it's good to envy someone like von Neumann. Of course I've always admired Francis Crick, who I think has a brain that effectively always asked the right questions, even though he didn't always get the right answers. I've always had a soft spot for and admired Leo Szilard, simply because he was sort of a representative of a world that I felt I had some kind of connection to.

Growing up in South Africa with some sort of connection to Europe gave it all a kind of fantastic background that one wanted to grasp because one felt in one's genes so to speak that one was connected to Europe. Of course one wasn't really. But there was that feeling of continuity with Europeans. When I met Leo Szilard I said, 'God, he looks like one of my uncles, the rich one!' It's the continuity to past worlds that I found fascinating. What I liked about Leo Szilard was his complete obliviousness to conventions and his complete focus on whatever came into his head."

… on the future

"I think that evolution will become an experimental subject, which will be wonderful. With that sort of knowledge we will even start to make new animals. I once gave a lecture on how to make a centaur by means other than transplantation surgery – which is the way the Greeks made centaurs – and what you would have to know in terms of developmental biology to create a six-limbed vertebrate, because that's what centaurs are. So I believe that we will move towards synthetic biology and I think that evolution is going to be *the* subject over the next twenty-five years. I think that there are going to be amazing discoveries that are going to tell us a lot about the past; we're going to be able to recapitulate the past. That will be a most exciting thing, and I think it will bring a new kind of synthetic approach to the subject of biology, which is now just being carved into smaller and smaller pieces.

The subject that will have to be reinvented is physiology. Nobody knows how to connect up all the molecular events to the actual functioning of an organism or an organ system. Physiology will have to be reinvented so that we can grasp how all this molecular stuff is embedded in the function of an organism. And the physiology that'll be the most interesting will be the physiology of the brain. There's tremendous discussion now on neurobiology and its theory, and what is consciousness, and so on. I'm one of the people who believes that the brain is a gland that excretes thoughts, and roughly speaking we have to find out how this excretion is carried out. I believe that we will get at this and I think it's going to be remarkable.

The subject I think is going to be most interesting, and which the new biology will open up is, in fact, the understanding of ourselves as organisms. For the first time we can now attack the fundamental biology of man, and I see the beginnings of trying to understand our evolution, and our history, and our culture, and our biology as one thing. So I believe that the great dream of the human sciences will be realised in the near future, because if it is indeed correct that the genome still retains evidence of past history, we should be able to recreate history beyond the written word and integrate it.

I think that the profession of science will change markedly over the next twenty-five years because it can't last in its present structure. The present structure is assumed on infinite growth. Every student expects to be a post-doc, and every post-doc expects to be an Assistant Professor with five graduate students. Every Assistant Professor expects to be an Associate Professor with eight post-docs and five students, and so on and so forth. That can't last. The industrial structure will have to change. What I think will happen in the future, is that people will do research for only part of their lives. I think that research – with very few exceptions – is really a job for young people, largely because, as I've said before, they have the ignorance that is necessary for it. It would be perfectly reasonable for people to do research for five years or eight years of their lives and then go on to do other things, like be doctors or farmers or something else in society. It may well be that doing biology will become like the old days of doing natural history, but with molecular tools.

The last thing I think is that DNA will come to occupy the centre of biology. I believe that man will destroy everything living on this planet and I would like to preserve everything in the form of DNA. To have a DNA treasure house – I like the term 'treasure house', rather than 'museum'. The idea would be collect the DNA of every living species and store it. Ultimately we could certainly sequence it, and find out what it is long after it's gone. But why trust to this terrible risk of survival of DNA in the form of a fossil when we could deliberately fossilise it? And then who knows, maybe in twenty years time, fifty years time, we could have our own Jurassic Park."

Index

A

acridine orange sensitivity 109–10
adaptor (transfer RNA) 66–7
AIDS virus research 159
Alembic Club, Oxford 39
Altman, Sydney 105
amber mutants 102, 103, 104
amino acids, coding for 30–1, 37, 38, 43–4, 46, 58–9, 64–5, 66
anthropology, early interest 15

B

Bacillus subtilis 149–50
bacterial conjugation (sexual exchange) 109–11
bacteriophage resistance 21–3, 27
bases of DNA 24–5, 43–7, 59, 69, 104
behavioural mutants 133, 134
Benzer, Seymour 47–9, 56, 57, 58, 59, 61, 64, 89, 90, 126
Berg, Paul 150
Bernal, Desmond 163
Bernstein, Hilliard 102
biochemistry, early interest in 9–10, 16
biology, early interest in 6, 7